STO ✓

Eugene Field

Young Poet

Illustrated by William Moyers

Eugene Field

Young Poet

By Kathryn Kilby Borland
and
Helen Ross Speicher

 THE **BOBBS-MERRILL** COMPANY, INC.
A SUBSIDIARY OF HOWARD W. SAMS & CO., INC.
Publishers · INDIANAPOLIS · NEW YORK

To "our" librarians,
who knew all the answers

Illustrations

Full Pages

Numerous smaller illustrations

Contents

CHILDHOOD
★★★★
OF FAMOUS
★★★★
® AMERICANS

★ ★

*Books by Kathryn Kilby Borland and
Helen Ross Speicher*

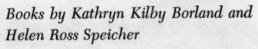

ALLEN PINKERTON: YOUNG DETECTIVE
EUGENE FIELD: YOUNG POET

Eugene Field

Young Poet

Tall Tales

"TELL US WHAT a leprechaun looks like, Temperance." Six-year-old Eugene Field winked at his younger brother, Roswell. The longer Temperance talked, the longer it would be until they had to go to bed. If there was anything Temperance liked to talk about, it was leprechauns. The boys loved her stories.

Temperance looked at Eugene. "Sure now, they'd be about as high as your knee," she said. " 'Tis not many that have ever seen a leprechaun. My grandfather did, but the little fellow got away. 'Twas a pity."

Eugene squirmed happily. "Tell us about it,"

he begged. The boys had heard this story many times, but it was still their favorite. Eugene even liked to hear the word "leprechaun." It had a magic sound.

Temperance laughed. "Sure, and you've heard the story so many times you could be telling it better than me." But she settled back in her chair. Her eyes had a faraway look.

"'Twas long ago. My grandfather thought he'd be the happiest man in all Ireland if he had the money to marry. But he was just learning his trade and had not two shillings to rub together. One fine spring day his feet carried him down a lane along a hedge. He scarce knew where he was. His mind was busy figuring how he might best earn some money. Eugene, if you're wanting to hear any more, I'll thank you not to stand on your head whilst I'm talking."

Eugene sat down quickly. "Don't stop now, Temperance. What did your grandfather hear?"

"As if you didn't know," Temperance said. "He heard the tap-tap-tapping of a tiny hammer. He thought to himself, 'Sure, and could it be a leprechaun?' He tiptoed up to the bush where he heard the noise and peeped under. And there, sure enough, was a tiny little man. He was sitting cross-legged and working on a wee pair of shoes."

"What did he wear?" Roswell asked eagerly.

"He was wearing a red coat with two rows of seven shiny buttons down the front. On his head he wore a little cap that came to a point at the top. He didn't see my grandfather watching him. Grandfather thought, 'If I can catch him, I'll have enough gold to marry and some left over.'"

"Did leprechauns have to give gold to anyone who caught them, even if they didn't like the person and didn't want to?" Eugene asked.

"That they did, unless, of course, they could

13

get away. They had many tricks. My grandfather crept up behind the wee man and caught him before the leprechaun could put his hammer down. ' 'Tis caught me ye have,' the little man said. 'Now I suppose ye'll be wantin' some gold. ' " Temperance paused.

14

"Go on," Eugene said eagerly.

" 'Yes,' says my grandfather. 'That I would, if you please. I'm in sore need of gold.' Then the wee man threw his hammer up in the air and said, 'If ye'll just hold my hammer whilst I push my way out of the hedge, we'll be on our way to find it.' My grandfather held up both hands to catch the hammer. The minute he took his hands off the leprechaun, the little fellow disappeared. Never did my grandfather see one again. He had to make what money he had the hard, long way like many another."

"We've looked and looked," Eugene complained, "but we've never seen even one leprechaun."

"If we do," Roswell said, "we'll never let him go till we get the gold. Now tell us about the banshees, Temperance."

"Isn't it bedtime?" Eugene asked.

"Bedtime? What's the matter, Eugene?"

asked Roswell. "Don't you want to hear a story about the banshees?"

"Banshees, is it?" Temperance laughed. She looked at the gold clock on the mantel. "Sure, and it's past your bedtime. You'd best be tucked in before your father comes. If he'd been home tonight, you'd have been in bed long before this."

The boys knew this was true. Since their mother had died the year before, their father had spent more and more time in his law office.

Temperance Moon had first come to live with the Fields when she was twelve years old. Now she took care of the boys. She fed them, mended their clothes, loved them, and told them stories. She didn't make them mind too much. She let them do what they wanted to.

"Eugene," whispered Roswell after Temperance had put out the light and closed the door.

"What?" Eugene asked sleepily.

"Why don't you like to hear about banshees?"

"I just don't," Eugene said. "Besides, sometimes I see them at night."

"You do?" asked Roswell. "What do they look like? What color are they?"

"What difference does it make what color they are when you're seeing them at night?" Eugene asked. "They're horrible. They moan and try to grab me. Let's not talk about them."

Mr. Field had barely had time to climb into bed and close his eyes that night when he heard a loud scream. Sleepily he climbed out of bed and ran down the hall.

He threw open the door to the boys' room. Roswell was sleeping quietly. Eugene was sleeping, but not quietly. He was screaming and waving his arms wildly in the air.

Mr. Field sat on the bed and gently shook Eugene awake. "What is it," he asked. "What were you dreaming about?"

17

"Banshees," said Eugene. "Banshees, screaming and crying and trying to grab me. When they come it means someone in the house is going to die." Eugene, his eyes frightened and full of tears, sat up in bed.

"Nonsense," said Mr. Field, patting Eugene's shoulder awkwardly. "Surely no one really believes in banshees in this year of 1856. Who's been teaching you nonsense? Has Temperance been telling you stories about banshees?"

Eugene didn't want Temperance to be in trouble. "Well, sir, she tells us stories because we ask her to. But it isn't her fault if we see things at night. She's good to us."

"Go to sleep," Mr. Fields said quietly. "We'll talk about it in the morning."

At the breakfast table the next morning the boys knew that something was troubling their father. He forgot to complain that his eggs were cold, as he usually did.

18

"Boys," he said finally. "I decided something very important last night. Your Aunt Mary and your cousin, Mary Field French, have written me several times lately. They have urged me to let you live with them in Massachusetts. I have said no before."

Eugene and Roswell looked at their father in sudden alarm. They seemed to know what he was going to say next.

"I did not want to break up our family," Mr. Field continued. "But my business keeps me from spending much time with you. We could never have managed without Temperance this past year. Now, however, you need to learn manners, mathematics and many other things she cannot teach you. Also, you need a firmer hand."

The boys did not want to leave their father, or Temperance, or St. Louis. They did not want to live in Massachusetts and be taught by two stern women. The idea sounded awful.

No More Leprechauns

"TICK-A-TOCK, tick-a-tock," the big grandfather clock in the hall said. Eugene Field thought it should be saying, "Tall old clock, tall old clock." The clock stood there, higher than his father.

It had been exciting to come all the way on the train from St. Louis, Missouri, with his father and brother. It had been fun to ride in the carriage through the dark to this big white house in Amherst, Massachusetts.

Now that he was here in bed, his eyelids kept closing. He wanted to stay awake and listen to what was being said downstairs. His relatives were discussing him and his brother.

Roswell hadn't tried to stay awake. He had just snuggled down in the big four-poster bed and gone fast asleep. When a boy was six, however, he should be able to stay awake.

"Now, Sister," Mr. Field's voice boomed, "I do not want my sons spoiled while they are staying with you."

A lady's fluttery voice answered, "Anything you say, of course. But they are such babies! How can you bear to leave them?" Eugene thought the voice must be Aunt Mary's.

A crisp answer came from Cousin Mary Field French. "All the more reason why he should leave them with us, Mother. A man should not try to rear children by himself."

Eugene's throat ached. Both his mother and Temperance were gone now. Soon his father would be gone. He felt homesick and lost.

"Furthermore, you are not to fill them with the superstititions of New England," Mr. Field continued. "I fear they have heard more folk stories already than they should have heard."

The next morning, Eugene could not even remember getting out of his clothes. He knew he had, however, because they lay neatly folded over a chair.

His blue eyes were full of interest as he looked expectantly at the sunshine streaming through the windows. He liked the crisp, white curtains and the neat, clean room.

"Wake up, Rozy," he called to the small heap huddled under the gay quilt.

"What's the matter?" a drowsy voice replied.

"Nothing is the matter. It's just that it's morning. We've got lots to do today."

"What all?" yawned Roswell.

"There's this big house to explore. I wonder how big the yard is."

Both boys jumped down from the high bed and ran to look out the open window. As they hung out over the sill, they could almost touch the branches of huge buttonball trees.

"Look at all those flowers, Rozy." Eugene could not remember when he had not loved flowers. Just then Aunt Mary opened the bedroom door and came in. Her starched dress crackled when she moved.

"Oh, my goodness, boys, don't fall out that window!" she exclaimed. She hurried across the room. "Gracious me, you don't want to get hurt the first day you're here!"

"Nor the second day, either," Eugene laughed. He let his long lanky legs drop back and down until he stood on the floor. He looked at his aunt with interest. She seemed upset over something. He wondered what it was.

"I do hope you slept well," she said finally.

"Yes, thank you," Eugene answered politely.

"I wish your father could have spent the day with you," she said sadly.

"Oh, didn't he stay?" wailed Roswell. Suddenly he missed his father very much.

"When will father come back?" Eugene asked.

"I really don't know. No one ever tells me anything." She seemed about to cry. Eugene didn't want her to cry.

"Who cares when he comes back?" he said. He really did care very much, but he was sure this was not the time to show it. Both Roxy and his aunt were pink around the eyes.

"Eugene! You really didn't mean to say that, I'm sure!" She didn't sound sure at all.

Eugene laughed. She was going to be fun to tease. "I mean I like it here with you. I like you too," he replied, and he suddenly realized he meant it. She smiled down at him forgivingly, and he smiled back.

"Come, boys, dress quickly," Cousin Mary called briskly. "Lizzie has breakfast ready."

There would be no nonsense about Cousin

Mary, Eugene decided, when he heard her voice. He wouldn't be able to tease her.

"What's Lizzie like?" he asked.

"Lizzie's our hired girl," Aunt Mary explained. "She comes in every day to cook and clean. Sometimes she's hard to get along with, so mind your manners."

"I'll race you to the stairs, Rozy," Eugene said, when his brother began to sniffle. "Last one's a slow poke and won't get any breakfast." This thought was so horrible that Roswell dressed almost as quickly as his brother.

They raced to the wide stairway. Eugene was delighted with the carved mahogany handrail. Swinging himself up on the flat surface, he sailed triumphantly downstairs.

Unfortunately he came to the end of the rail just as Lizzie walked down the hall, and he landed squarely in the middle of her starched apron. She teetered unsteadily and finally sat down hard on the floor. The pitcher and glasses which she was carrying on a tray fell to the floor, and their contents were spilled.

The two sat and looked at each other for a long minute. Lizzie was the first to speak.

"Humph!" she exploded. "So this is what's come to live with us, is it?"

"I really am sorry," Eugene said, but he couldn't help laughing. Lizzie did look funny, sitting on the floor, with her thin legs in their blue and white striped stockings straight out like sticks.

"Humph!" Lizzie said. "No manners at all."

"Sure and a pixie must have tripped us both," Eugene replied. His blue eyes sparkled.

"Now none of that Irish nonsense your father told us about," Cousin Mary warned.

"It was the wee folk," Eugene insisted.

Lizzie glared at him. "The only wee folk I know are about to get their breeches birched."

26

"You'll have to catch them first," Eugene laughed gleefully.

"Eugene, I'm sure you don't mean to speak so to your elders," Aunt Mary said. Again she looked doubtful and didn't sound quite sure.

"But the little people——" Eugene began.

"That's quite enough, Eugene." Cousin Mary was firm. Someone had to be. "I can see that you do need lessons in manners."

Eugene's spirits sank. The happy, tingling excitement of the morning left him. He missed Temperance and her easy-going ways. She let them eat when they felt like it, not when the clock said it was time. She liked a good rousing race through the house.

Life with these three women was going to be too strict to suit him. Slowly Eugene got to his feet. He joined the others at breakfast.

The day passed quickly in spite of Eugene's fears that nothing could be fun here. He was too lighthearted to worry or to be discouraged by anything for long.

He and Roswell roamed from room to room in the huge house. They looked at the pictures of trees and leaves on the wallpaper. They counted the dark panels in the high walls of the rooms. They noticed the wax flowers on the shelves of the many whatnots. There were dried grasses in crystal vases.

"Grasses in glasses, glasses for grasses," Eugene chanted. He liked to put words together and to make rhymes.

Roswell followed closely at his heels as they pushed past the heavy front door. The boys walked all around the big white frame house. They took a long time, because they stopped to examine anything that interested them.

As they came near the kitchen, they smelled something delicious. The sweet fragrance led them to three warm blueberry pies set out on

the pantry window ledge to cool. They stood
looking at the pies and smelling them until their
mouths watered.

"Three pies! We'd never eat all those!" said
Eugene, his eyes sparkling.

Roswell looked up at him eagerly. "Wouldn't we?" he asked hopefully.

"Never! Two pies are all we could possibly need. Lizzie probably made an extra pie the way Temperance made us little sugar pies."

"Oh, I miss Temperance!" Roswell's lip started to quiver.

"Suppose one pie disappeared," Eugene said. "They'd never miss it."

"What would happen to it?" Roswell asked. He was interested in spite of himself.

"We would." Eugene chuckled. Looking around, he saw a bench under an apple tree.

"Help me drag that bench over here, Rozy. It's not very far. Then I can stand on it. I think I can just reach that pie."

Carefully the boys pulled the old bench under the window. Eugene reached up from the bench for the warm blueberry pie. Slipping it under his jacket, he hurried away.

"We'll hide it in our room, and tonight we can have a picnic," Eugene planned. Roswell, who was trotting along trustingly after his brother, pouted.

"I want to eat it now," he said.

"It's too near dinner time. Anyway, we'd get caught now. It'll be more fun in the dark tonight," Eugene insisted. "Come on."

Silently the two small robbers crept back into the house. They tiptoed upstairs to hide the pie in their closet. It was still warm, and it did smell good. Eugene almost wished he had not decided to wait.

Then Cousin Mary's clear voice called, "Wash your hands, boys, and come downstairs."

"See, I told you so," Eugene hissed to Roswell. "I'm glad we didn't start eating it."

At the dinner table everyone seemed to be unusually quiet. Aunt Mary was troubled about something. Cousin Mary paid no attention to them at all. Lizzie rattled dishes and banged pans in the pantry between courses. When she brought in large pieces of blueberry pie, Eugene almost burst with his secret.

"Blueberry pie is my favorite kind," he said, as he picked up his fork.

Lizzie had a scowl on her face that would have soured cream. She retorted, "Happen you know something about that third pie!"

"Yes, I saw who took it," Eugene answered, smiling as everyone stared at him. Roswell looked startled.

"Why didn't you call me then?" Lizzie asked, glaring at him suspiciously.

"Didn't you hear me?" Eugene asked.

"I might have if you'd really called." Lizzie was certainly hard to fool.

"Who was it?" asked Aunt Mary, her voice shaking. "We've never had thieves here before."

"It was a little man." Eugene was gleeful.

32

"What did this little man look like?" asked Cousin Mary quietly.

"Oh, he was small and dark, and he reached a great long arm up to get the pie."

Aunt Mary began to look quite frightened at the thought of such a character. Lizzie wasn't afraid, though.

"You don't say!" she said. "And what was your little man wearing?"

"A red coat," Eugene said.

Cousin Mary looked surprised. "A red coat!" she exclaimed.

Eugene was having a wonderful time. They were all waiting to hear what he would say next. "Yes. There were seven silver buttons in two rows on the coat. He wore a tiny pointed hat, too, and tiny green shoes."

"A likely tale!" Lizzie snorted. "And I suppose he told you his name?"

"No," Eugene admitted truthfully.

Roswell had heard Temperance describe this little man many a time. He shouted out joyfully, "He's a leprechaun!"

"Leprechaun, now!" Lizzie said in disgust. "I'd have believed you quicker if you'd said 'The Headless Horseman.'" She pointed an accusing finger at the blue stain on Eugene's jacket. "Little man, was it? Pointed hat, did you say? More likely it was a pointed head, and that one yours, I'd say."

Eugene jumped up from his chair. "You guessed it, Lizzie," he shrieked happily. "I did take the pie, but I fooled you for a little while, didn't I, now?"

"Stealing things that don't belong to you isn't any kind of a joke, young man." Lizzie glared at him as if she'd like to turn him over her knee. Then she turned back toward the kitchen, her head held high.

"Oh, Lizzie," Eugene ran after her. "Don't

be cross. I didn't eat the pie. It's in my room. I'll get it for you." He raced upstairs. His eyes had been so gleeful that Lizzie had to smile in spite of herself.

Aunt Mary spoke up hastily. "Oh, Lizzie, he didn't mean any harm, I'm sure."

"Mother, he can't be allowed to think that deceit and stealing are permitted here. His father expects us to control him and teach him. He is lively and full of fun, but we must help him to be dependable and honest, too." Cousin Mary looked as if one morning with this active boy had already tired her. She could see that life with Eugene Field in the house was not going to be the least bit quiet or dull.

Too Much Music

"HERE, POOG! HERE, POOG!" Eugene called. He was lying on his stomach just outside the chickenyard fence.

"Whatever are you doing, Eugene?" Lizzie was coming out of the kitchen door. She had a pan of chicken feed in her hand.

"Sh!" Eugene said. "Poog's just learning her name. Don't interrupt!"

"Forever more," Lizzie said. "Whoever heard of giving a chicken a name? I hope you don't hold your breath till she answers."

"Which one's Poog?" Roswell asked.

"The big one with the dark brown wings,"

Eugene answered. Then he called again, "Here, Poog," and the big chicken raised its head and ran across the yard toward Eugene.

"See!" Eugene exclaimed. "She does know her name. She likes to have a name."

"More likely she heard the feed rattling in the pan," Lizzie sniffed. Eugene sighed. Lizzie was very hard to convince.

"Come into the house now and get dressed," Lizzie commanded. "We're going to eat supper early so your Cousin Mary can take you to the concert. Hurry up!"

Eugene and Roswell were much more interested in watching the chickens than in going to a concert. Each of them threw a handful of feed to the chickens.

"What did you name the rest of them?" asked Roswell, throwing more feed.

"Finniken, Minniken, Dump and Boog," Eugene answered. "The fat one is named Dump, and that little one over there is named Boog. Soon all of them will know their names."

"Outlandish names," Lizzie said. She threw a handful of feed to the chickens.

"I like the way they sound," Eugene said. "They sound like chickens' names."

A big dog with a long tail and short hair came running into the yard. "Hello, Dooley," Eugene greeted it.

"Dooley?" Lizzie said. "Name's Fido and always has been."

"But he has an Irish face," Eugene said, "and he ought to have an Irish name."

"I never saw such a boy for pets and foolish notions," Lizzie said. She tossed out the last handful of feed. "Now, come into the house this instant and get into some civilized clothes. We have to hurry!"

Eugene decided this would not be a good time to tell her about the baby squirrel he had found

38

that morning. Anyway, Cousin Mary would be the one to ask if he could keep it. Or maybe Aunt Mary would be better yet. She always looked anxious, but she never said no.

"This instant, Eugene," Lizzie said.

"Good-by, Poog," Eugene said.

"Land sakes," Lizzie said. "Next you'll be wanting to take that chicken to the concert. Come along, now."

"A chicken might like music," Eugene said thoughtfully. "Dogs do. Dooley likes Irish songs best. Just watch!"

Eugene whistled an Irish jig on his way to the house. Dooley ran in circles. He barked excitedly and wagged his tail. Lizzie followed them, shaking her head.

Eugene was happy to be going to the concert. His father had sometimes taken the boys to band concerts at home. Eugene could always hear the music in his head long after the concert was over. He couldn't understand why Cousin Mary said Roswell was too young to go along. Father had usually taken him.

He didn't like Cousin Mary's idea of civilized clothes. His jacket was too hot. His high starched collar dug into his skin. He had gone barefoot all day, and his shoes were pinching his feet. Cousin Mary certainly set more store by looking nice than she did in being comfortable.

"That jacket doesn't fit just right, does it?" Aunt Mary asked as they were leaving. "Both sides don't look alike, some way."

"Oh, don't fuss, Mother," Cousin Mary said. "We'll be late, unless we hurry."

"Will the concert be in the park, Cousin Mary?" Eugene asked. They were walking down the street in the warm summer twilight.

"In the park?" Cousin Mary asked. "Goodness, no. It will be in the Boltwoods' house."

40

Eugene thought the Boltwoods' house must be very large indeed if a band concert could be held in it. The concerts he'd attended in St. Louis had been held outdoors.

It was indeed a big house. It had the widest stairway Eugene had ever seen. He thought how much he would like to slide down that smooth, curved bannister just once.

On the walls of the rooms were many pictures of rather cross-looking ladies and gentlemen. They looked as uncomfortable in their frames as he felt in his tight shoes. Cousin Mary introduced him to many ladies and gentlemen. They were all very elegantly dressed, but he didn't see anyone in a band uniform.

Finally Cousin Mary led him into a long room where the guests were sitting on stiff little gold chairs. The chairs did not look comfortable, and they weren't. Everyone was quiet now. Still Eugene did not see any band.

"Where's the band?" he whispered.

"There's no band," Cousin Mary whispered back. "This will be chamber music."

"What's chamber music?" Eugene asked.

Just then four men came in. Two were carrying violins. One carried a big cello. One carried what Cousin Mary said was a viola.

"Viola? I like the word," Eugene said. "It sounds like a flower."

"Hush," said Cousin Mary.

For a few minutes the music sounded pretty, but it didn't seem to have much tune. Eugene, trying to be comfortable, slid down in his chair, so that his feet touched the floor.

"Sit up, Eugene," Cousin Mary whispered.

He sat up. He was tired of holding his hand over the bulge in his jacket, but he had to do it. Cousin Mary didn't seem to notice.

The men played and played. Eugene sighed. Maybe they'd never stop.

His legs itched in their warm hose. He scratched his right ankle with his left foot.

"Stop that, Eugene," Cousin Mary whispered. Eugene stopped, but he was feeling hotter and more uncomfortable every minute.

Finally the men stopped playing. Eugene smiled happily. Then they leafed through some more music and began to play again. He'd been right. They were never going to stop. He'd have to sit there on that little gold chair for the rest of his life.

He looked at Cousin Mary. She looked very happy. He guessed she wouldn't care if they did have to sit there all night.

Maybe if he could think about something else the time would go more quickly. He'd think about words. When he heard a new word, he liked to think about it. He'd heard quite a few new words at Amherst.

"Wash" wasn't a new word, but he and Roswell had certainly heard it often enough in the two days they'd been here. "Wash, wash, wash." It had a wet, soapy sound. "Must" was another word they had heard about fifty times a day.

"Must, must, must," he thought. It had a dull sound. It rhymed with dust, which there wasn't much of in the Amherst house. "Dust, dust, dust," he thought. His eyelids kept closing. His head kept nodding.

Suddenly Eugene woke up. How long had he been asleep? Quickly he felt for the bulge in his jacket. It was gone, as he had known it would be. Cousin Mary was still smiling. The men were still playing.

Carefully he began to look about the big room. Soon he saw the thing which didn't belong at the concert. A bushy brown tail stuck out from under the long blue skirt of a lady in the row ahead of him. He stared, fascinated.

"Fuzzy, please, please sit still," Eugene

thought. Of course he knew he shouldn't have brought the squirrel to the concert. But somehow he had never found the right time to ask if he could keep it.

He hadn't known what to do except to take Fuzzy with him. Besides, what Lizzie had said made him wonder if squirrels liked music. It must be they liked this kind better than he did. At least Fuzzy had snuggled quietly in his pocket for a long time.

Now the brown tail began to twitch. The lady in the blue dress moved her feet. She looked down at the floor with a puzzled expression. But Fuzzy had moved.

Now he was sitting on the train of a brown lace dress. Pretty soon that lady, too, moved her feet and looked surprised. Fuzzy ran over the feet of a tall man next to the lady in the brown dress, but he was gone before the man saw him. Still the men played. Even Cousin

Mary looked a little tired, Eugene thought. Only his interest in Fuzzy kept Eugene awake.

Finally someone saw Fuzzy. People began whispering and pointing. Some of them were smiling, but most of them were frowning.

Fuzzy was getting bolder all the time. He leaped and whirled and ran in circles. Finally he ran toward the door of the big room. Eugene didn't know what to do. If he just sat there, perhaps nobody would ever guess that Fuzzy belonged to him. But if he did that, he'd never get Fuzzy back, and somebody might hurt the little squirrel.

Maybe if he didn't stand up, nobody would see him follow Fuzzy. Quickly he slid from his chair. He began crawling on his hands and knees toward the door. He'd been wrong about nobody noticing, though. By the time he got to the doorway, Cousin Mary was behind him. Her face was very red.

"Eugene Field!" she said, "Have you taken leave of your senses?"

They could hear screaming from across the hall. A big table in the dining room was covered with a long white cloth. On it were platters of little cakes and thin sandwiches.

Fuzzy was on the table running wildly about. He knocked over cups and saucers. His tail brushed over the plate of little cakes. Two women were standing by the table screaming. You'd think they'd never seen a squirrel before, Eugene thought with disgust. Suddenly Fuzzy saw himself in the enormous silver tea urn at the end of the table. He sat back and looked at his reflection. He was sure that he had found a friend. Quickly Eugene caught the little squirrel and held him gently.

Eugene thought that he and Aunt Mary would never be through apologizing. They apologized to the musicians. They apologized to the hostess. They apologized to the women who screamed. They apologized to the other guests.

"Apologize, apologize," thought Eugene. The word certainly had a stiff, uncomfortable sound. He didn't like it.

"Eugene Field," Cousin Mary said as they walked home. "You've given us more trouble in two days than we've ever had in two years before. You must learn to think."

"I'm sorry, Cousin Mary," Eugene asked. He really was sorry. Somehow, things had a way of not turning out the way he had planned them.

Harry Brown and Elijah

EUGENE AND Roswell walked slowly down the street in the warm spring sunshine. The windows of the school were open. The two boys could hear the girls inside, reciting their spelling lesson.

"Glory, Roswell," said Eugene, "aren't you glad we can take lessons with different professors instead of being stuck in a school all day? Listen to those poor girls!"

"Especially in a school for girls," Roswell agreed. "What could be worse?"

"I'll bet they never have a day in school when the teachers are too busy to teach them either.

50

It was wonderful luck that our teachers had to do other things, so they couldn't teach us today," Eugene said.

"What shall we do instead?" Roswell asked. "How about walking past Howlands' and picking some cherries? The Howlands are the only ones who don't make a fuss if boys and birds eat a few of their cherries."

Eugene shook his head. "Cherries aren't ripe yet. We'll have to wait."

"We could play in the Dickinsons' hayloft."

"Not enough hay in it now. Besides, Miss Vinnie got pretty cross last time."

"Would you like to swing?"

"Would you?"

"Not much," Roswell said. Usually the boys could think of something to do.

"Here comes Harry Brown," Eugene said. "We'll find out what he's doing. Maybe he has a good idea we haven't thought about."

51

Harry, who was barefooted, was kicking up little clouds of dust and watching them settle.

"Hello, Harry," Roswell called. "What are you doing?"

"Nothing," Harry said. "What are you doing?"

"Nothing."

Harry joined his friends, and the three boys walked slowly down the street.

"Look," Eugene said, "the door to the Baptist Church is open."

"Just look at that big long old bell rope," Roswell said. "What do you think would happen if we pulled on it?"

"I think we'd get in trouble," Harry said.

"I don't mean that. Would you swing through the air when the bell rang?"

Eugene's eyes brightened. "Yes, of course you would," he said. "It would be like flying. Now that would really be something to do."

Roswell's eyes were wide. "You wouldn't!"

"Yes I would," Eugene said, "but I don't think I could reach it. Harry's lucky. He could reach it. He's the one who can fly."

Harry looked doubtful. "I don't know," he said. "I'm not sure I want to."

"You mean you don't want to fly?"

"Maybe he's afraid to," Roswell said.

Suddenly Harry ran into the entry of the church. He jumped up to reach the end of the heavy rope and hung on.

Before Eugene and Roswell could close their mouths, Harry shot up out of sight. One minute he was swinging from the rope. The next minute they could see his feet at the top of the open door. Then he was gone. The bells began to clang noisily.

Eugene and Roswell stood for a moment staring at the empty doorway. Then they ran toward the door. The janitor ran out.

"What are you boys doing? Don't ever do it again," he scolded.

"Harry's gone," Eugene said breathlessly. "He rang the bell and disappeared."

"He'd better disappear, and so had you," said the janitor. He slammed the door and started down the walk. The boys were afraid of the janitor. They ran down the street and hid behind a lilac bush.

As soon as the sound of the janitor's heavy footsteps grew fainter, the boys looked out cautiously. "He's turned a corner," Eugene said. "Let's go back and find Harry."

The heavy door was locked. "Harry! Harry!" they called, pounding on the church door. But there was no answer.

They walked around to the back of the church where they found a little door open. They stepped into the dark, cool back entry. Then they went into the sanctuary. It was very still there.

They'd never been in the church by themselves before. They tiptoed up the aisle to the door opening into the front entry. The bell rope hung down stiffly, as if no one had ever touched it.

"Harry! Harry!" they called. They could hear small birds flying about overhead, but there was no answer to their call.

"Eugene," Roswell whispered, "remember the story in Sunday school about how Elijah was snatched up into heaven? Do you think Harry——"

"Harry Brown?" Eugene asked. "Don't be silly, Roswell!'"

"Then where is he?"

"Oh, he's all right," Eugene said, but he didn't sound very sure. "Maybe we'd better go home and tell Cousin Mary about him. Or maybe Aunt Mary would be the best one to tell."

The boys walked home quietly. They wondered where Harry was and if they would ever see him again. As they started up the front walk, a tall, heavy man came out the front door.

"Mr. Sam!" both boys called. "Mr. Sam!"

Sam Jones was Aunt Mary's son. He lived in Chicago, but he often visited his mother. He smiled at the boys. "If it isn't Eugene and Roswell," he said. "I need help. There seems to be something in one of my pockets that doesn't belong there. Will you see if you can help me find out what it is?"

The boys were glad to help. Mr. Sam had been in Amherst once before since they had been there. He liked to surprise them with gifts, both large and small. Cousin Mary had said he would spoil the boys, but Mr. Sam had answered that he wasn't there enough to spoil them.

The things which were making his pocket heavy turned out to be two shiny pocket knives. The boys gazed at them with delight.

"Sit down," Mr. Sam said. He took a piece of

56

wood out of another pocket. "I'll show you how
to carve a bear."

The boys were fascinated. They forgot all
about Harry. Just as the shape of a bear was
beginning to emerge from the piece of wood,
Cousin Mary opened the door.

"Whatever are you doing out there, boys?"
she asked. "You should have been all ready
for dancing class by now."

Suddenly Eugene remembered. "Cousin
Mary," he said, "I've got to tell you something."

"Not now," she said. "March right upstairs
and get your good suits on."

"But Cousin Mary——"

"March!" she said.

"It's about Harry," Eugene called over his
shoulder as he climbed the stairs.

"You'll see him at dancing class."

"No we won't," Eugene said. "He won't be
there. We don't know——"

"Is that all?" Cousin Mary said. She disappeared down the hallway.

Dancing class was awful. After the boys got there they had to put on white gloves and patent leather shoes.

Miss Green lined the boys up in one row and the girls in another. Then her sister played the piano while she counted, "One, two, three, step. One, two, three, step." She tried to get them to move in time to the music. The girls giggled. The boys tried to step on one another's feet. Miss Green made them take partners.

Then she frowned. "We're not coming out even," she said. "Somebody isn't here."

"It's Harry Brown," a little girl in a white dress with a blue sash said.

"Does anyone know where Harry is?" Miss Green asked the children.

Roswell looked at Eugene. "We think he might have been snatched up into Heaven," he said. Luckily the music was too loud for Miss Green to hear. The second time Roswell opened his mouth, Eugene shook his head. Just then there was a knock on the door. When Miss Green opened it, Harry Brown stood there. He had a bandage on his head, and he looked pale.

"If you're all right, Harry," she said, looking at him anxiously, "we can begin. Stand over there behind Eugene."

"What happened?" Eugene whispered. It was hard to hear with the music playing.

"—right up into the belfry," Harry said.

"One, two, three, step," Miss Green said.

"How did you get down?"

"Slid down the rope. Ran out the back door."

"And a one and a two and a three. Eugene, if you paid more attention, you would not always end up on the wrong foot."

"Was it like flying?" Eugene had to know.

"Sort of. My mother said you were the worst boy in town. I'm not supposed to speak to you for a whole week, maybe never."

The music had stopped. Harry had told the whole class what his mother had said. Eugene sighed. Once more things didn't seem to have turned out exactly the way he had planned.

Mouse in the House

"It's such a long way up to Grandmother's front door," Roswell said unhappily.

Nine-year-old Eugene didn't think the distance was too great. He liked the gravelled walk which led from the gate in the white picket fence to the green door of the house. He noticed a humming-bird hovering over a pale pink rose. He looked at the funny little faces of the pansies, which had been planted in a double row on each side of the walk.

"Come along, boys," the driver of the town hack called. He had already stacked their boxes and bags neatly on the steps and was banging the curious little brass knocker on the door. Eugene liked the sound which it made.

It was a hot August day. Both boys were tired after the long trip from Cousin Mary's house. Grandmother Field had invited them to visit her in Newfane, Vermont.

"General Martin Field," Eugene read from the brass door plate. He wondered if his grandfather would have been out at the gate waiting if he'd still been alive. This big, two-story house was too quiet.

"Quite quiet, queerly quiet," Eugene chanted. He still liked the sound of certain words. The door opened suddenly. A stately old lady with white hair greeted them solemnly.

"Good evening, Eugene, Roswell. Come in, boys. You are most welcome." But she didn't put her arms around them and kiss them as Aunt Mary had. The hack driver set the boys' bags inside the house and returned to his horses.

Eugene and Roswell looked about them curiously. The house was paneled in some dark wood. They sniffed the clean smell of furniture polish. From the kitchen came the fragrance of newly-baked bread and of roasting meat. Both boys suddenly realized that they were very hungry.

Eugene noticed his grandmother's wax flowers. Everyone he knew had wax flowers in their halls and company rooms. Lizzie dusted Aunt Mary's every day with a big brown feather duster. Temperance had just bought new ones whenever the old ones became dusty.

These were different. They were tiny pink moss roses, and they were under a glass cover. Eugene had never before seen flowers enclosed. How awful to be so closed in!

Slowly his hand slid down into his pocket. Mabel, his white mouse, stirred restlessly. She was cooped up in his coat, but she could run up his collar if she wanted to. The little pink flowers couldn't get out.

Mabel sniffed at his fingers. From his first look at Grandmother Field's house, Eugene had known he had been wrong to bring Mabel with him. This spotless house would not welcome a guest mouse. He must be careful to keep the small pink nose out of sight. His long slender fingers soothed the tiny animal. He breathed a sigh of relief as Mabel sat still again.

"Eugene, you are not listening to me." His grandmother's voice was raised slightly.

"Oh, I'm sorry," Eugene answered.

"I was suggesting that you and Roswell go up to your room at the top of the stairs."

"Yes, Grandmother," both boys answered.

Roswell quickly scampered up the dark stairway. Eugene went slowly, one foot dragging behind the other. He was still thinking about the imprisoned flowers.

"Eugene, do you not feel well?" Grandmother Field asked, coming closer to him. His staring eyes worried her.

"Oh, I'm all right, thank you, Grandmother."

"Then stop biting your fingernails and hurry," she said sternly.

With a quick change of mood, Eugene ran up the last few steps. Roswell was already pouring water out of the big blue and white china pitcher into the washbowl on the stand.

Eugene looked across the room at the tall narrow windows. In front of him was their four-poster bed. Quickly he somersaulted over it and landed in front of the windows.

Roswell stopped dabbling his fingers in the lukewarm water and watched.

"Try it, Rozy," the older boy urged.

Roswell didn't quite get over the bed and managed to wrinkle the neat cover and fall against Eugene. Both boys bumped to the floor.

Scuffling like puppies, they thrashed about happily and made a great deal of noise.

Downstairs Mrs. Field raised her eyebrows in surprise at the sounds above her. It had been a long time since there had been any children in her house.

A soft Chinese gong announced supper. The thumping stopped. There was silence for a moment. Then two heavy pairs of boys' boots raced noisily down the stairs. Grandmother Field sighed. Surely her own sons had never made such a hubbub.

"Are we late?" Roswell asked fearfully.

"We hurried," Eugene said hopefully.

"I can see that," their grandmother told them. Their hair, which was very wet, was plastered down. A few wet spots showed on their coat collars.

"After this, take time to tidy yourselves properly," she said sternly.

"We will," both boys promised meekly.

Eugene reached into his pocket for the comforting touch of Mabel. His grandmother, leading the way into the dining room, didn't see his frightened face. She didn't hear him whisper excitedly to Roswell, "Mabel's gone."

"Where?" asked Roswell.

"How should I know?"

"What will you do?" Roswell asked as they walked down the long hall.

"Look for her, of course, after supper."

"How did she get away?" Roswell asked.

"She probably fell out of my pocket while I was somersaulting across the bed."

Eugene's blue eyes crinkled up at the corners as he laughed quietly. "She's probably already gone to bed, don't you suppose?"

Roswell smiled, too, at the thought of the tiny mouse asleep in their big bed.

Eugene always had a pet of some sort. He

was forever taking some kind of animal out of his pockets—chipmunks, baby rabbits, grasshoppers, lizards—anything he could catch. Sometimes he tamed them, as he had tamed Mabel. Other times they just ran away and turned up later in odd places.

After supper, Grandmother Field showed them through the huge old house. She told them stories of their father when he was a little boy. She let them see certificates he had won later at school. He had been the best speller, the best Latin student, and the best speaker.

"I was very proud of him," she said, her eyes shining. "Your father studied hard."

Eugene thought of all the times Cousin Mary had let him study his lessons outdoors. Most of these times he had not bothered to open his books. It was so pleasant just to lie on his back and watch the clouds drift across the sky. He loved to smell the sweetness of clover in the sun. Books didn't tell about the lightness of butterflies as they danced from cardinal flower to Queen Anne's lace.

He couldn't count the number of little animals he had found in the fields. He could tame almost any of them if he tried.

That reminded him of Mabel. Where had she gone? As the boys followed their grandmother through the house, Eugene peeked behind curtains. He stooped to look under chairs. He raised cushions as he passed. He didn't really expect to find Mabel in his bed. He knew she liked to explore as well as he did.

"Rozy, go on ahead with Grandmother, and keep talking to her," Eugene finally whispered.

"Why?" the younger boy asked.

"So I can look for Mabel without having Grandmother notice," Eugene said softly.

"I thought you said she'd gone to bed."

"I hope she has, but maybe she didn't," whis-

pered Eugene. "Can you imagine Grandmother's face if she found my mouse in her bed?"

Both boys shuddered at the thought. But Mabel didn't come out of hiding. Eugene could picture all sorts of adventures for his small mouse with her white whiskers.

"Eugene, were you not taught respect for the property of others?" Mrs. Field was shocked at the peepings and peerings of her grandson.

"Wh-what do you mean?" stammered Eugene, knowing quite well. He had hoped Grandmother wouldn't notice what he was doing.

"Have you not been taught that a gentleman does not peep under pillows and open other people's doors unless asked?"

"Oh, yes, I know about that," Eugene admitted, his face red with embarrassment.

"I'd never have suspected it," his grandmother said sternly. "We will have no more of such behavior. Perhaps you and Roswell would like to go out on the porch and sit on the steps until bedtime. You have not seen my flowers."

"Could we play some games in the yard?"

"Certainly not!" his grandmother answered sharply. "Games are not for the Sabbath."

"But this is Saturday," Eugene argued. "It's not Sunday yet."

"In my house the Sabbath begins at six o'clock Saturday evening, young man. My household works hard to prepare a proper day of rest. My lamps are trimmed, my food is ready, and my rooms are swept. Perhaps we had best start our Bible reading this evening instead of waiting until tomorrow. I shall get the Bible which your father and uncle read when they were children." Grandmother Field closed the door firmly behind her. By the tone the boys knew it would not be wise to argue any more.

"Grandmother was really angry with you for peeking under things," Roswell pointed out.

"I guess I shouldn't have looked for Mabel," Eugene said sadly, "but I know she will be lonesome all by herself."

"Maybe she'll find a Vermont mouse for a friend," Roswell said hopefully.

"Maybe." Eugene was thinking of something else now. "Rozy, do you remember what Grandmother told us about these buildings around here? They all belong to her, don't they?"

"That's what she was telling us when you had your head under that sofa," Roswell laughed.

Eugene looked toward the side yard and back to a little white building. The building had small columns that reminded him of pictures he'd seen in a book about Greek temples. It faced the village common, a great green lawn in the center of Newfane.

"Is that a playhouse?" he asked.

"No, it's the law office Grandfather built. Father and Uncle Charles studied law there."

"That's the sassafras tree Grandmother planted near it," Eugene said eagerly. "See, the leaves look like mittens."

"There's an icehouse, a woodshed, a barn, a carriage house, and Grandfather's museum. Grandmother pointed them all out." Roswell was beginning to yawn.

"I'd like to see inside the museum," Eugene murmured. "I think I'd have liked to have talked to Grandfather. He collected lots of things—birds' nests, shells, rocks, and fossils."

"What are fossils?" asked Roswell drowsily.

"They are rocks with a print of something on them—a leaf or a fish skeleton. There are supposed to be all kinds of fossils around here. Maybe I can start a collection, too."

When Grandmother opened the door, Roswell was already yawning. "Bedtime, boys," she said firmly. "We'll let the Bible reading wait until tomorrow when you're rested."

74

"Yes, ma'am," agreed Roswell sleepily.

Eugene followed his grandmother's skirts closely as he went up the long, unlighted stairway. Somehow it seemed darker here than at Cousin Mary's. Suddenly he thought of gremlins and wee folk. He hadn't thought of them since he and Roswell had come to Cousin Mary's.

Roswell pushed drowsily ahead. Nothing but bed interested him. As their grandmother tucked them into bed, he was almost asleep. Eugene, however, was wide-awake. He pulled the covers up over his head. He wished the corners of the room didn't have so many shadows in them.

He reached out to touch Mabel, as he always did before he went to sleep. Then he remembered. Mabel was gone. He only hoped he would find her before Grandmother did.

Company for
Dinner

IT RAINED during the night, and Sunday morning was unseasonably cloudy, windy, and cool. At breakfast Grandmother told the boys they must be ready to leave for church at the sound of the first bell.

"I have never been late for church," she said. She frowned at them as if they were certain to make her late for the first time. The boys helped Grandmother carry the breakfast dishes to the kitchen, but no dishes were ever washed on Sunday.

When the bells began chiming from the Congregational Church across the square, Grandmother gave the boys one more inspection. She made sure their blouses were tucked in and their hair was properly plastered down. Then she put on her little black cape and they started down the long front walk.

Eugene thought Grandmother looked very handsome in her black cape and bonnet. Over her arm she carried a huge black velvet bag decorated with flowers made of beads.

"You may carry my footstove, Eugene," she said. "It will be drafty in church this morning." The footstove looked like a little square box. She showed him that there was a place in it for hot coals.

Grandmother was right. The church was cold and drafty. Very little light came through the tall windows today. The straight-backed seats seemed harder than the ones in Amherst, too. The Fields had been almost the first to arrive. When other people came in, they went straight to their seats. They didn't smile and nod at each other as people did at the Amherst church. There Miss Vinnie Dickinson usually had a little bouquet of flowers to hand to someone. Mrs. Deacon Sweetser always had peppermints to pass out to boys with dry throats.

By the time the service started Eugene's teeth were chattering. Roswell's lips looked blue.

"I'm cold," Eugene whispered to Grandmother.

"Nonsense," she said, not taking her feet from the footstove. "You're only boys. Only old ladies are cold."

The service seemed longer than the one in Amherst, too. When Eugene saw Grandmother pull a cracker out of her big bag he thought, "She knows we're hungry." But Grandmother nibbled on the cracker slowly, not looking at the boys. Eugene knew without asking that she would say that only ladies were hungry. He guessed it

78

was proper for old ladies to nibble crackers in church, but wicked for little boys.

He thought about the difference between life in Amherst and life in Newfane. Roswell and he had thought Cousin Mary was strict, after Temperance's easygoing ways. They had soon found, though, that if they minded their manners and were on time for meals, they could do just about whatever they wanted to.

Grandmother knew what they were doing all the time. If she didn't like it, they had to do something else. Grandmother loved them in her way, but she wanted them to be perfect. Eugene was afraid he would never suit her.

After the service there was a great deal of handshaking to be done. Some of the people they met said Eugene looked exactly like his father. Others said neither of the boys looked like any of the Fields and seemed to consider the two brothers unfortunate for this reason.

Mrs. Field invited Mrs. Deacon Ranney and Mrs. Brill to have dinner with her and the boys. These two old ladies were the ones who had looked the sorriest because Eugene and Roswell did not look like their father. Both ladies wore black silk dresses which rustled when they walked. Eugene did not think they looked nearly as handsome as his grandmother.

The conversation at dinner was not very interesting. Mostly it was about Mrs. Deacon Ranney's daughter, who lived way out West in Ohio. Eugene tried to say that he and Roswell had lived even further west, in St. Louis, but Grandmother told him not to interrupt.

Finally Mrs. Deacon Ranney looked at Eugene and asked, "What do you do all day, Eugene?" It seemed to him that her black eyes were burning a hole through him.

"Well, I——"

"Just remember, boy, the devil finds work for

idle hands to do. You should try to work and study as hard as your father did."

Eugene was indignant. She seemed sure he had idle hands before he even answered.

"How I remember their father at his age," she said to Grandmother. "Ready for college at eleven, wasn't he?"

"Yes, indeed," answered Grandmother proudly. "Even at that age he could read Latin, French, and German extremely well."

"My, my," said Mrs. Deacon Ranney, looking at Eugene disapprovingly and shaking her head. "What languages can you read?"

"Just English," said Eugene in a small voice. He was thinking about all the times he had watched the clouds instead of studying.

"Your father was ready to practice law when he was seventeen years old," said Mrs. Brill.

Eugene looked down at the floor so they would not see the tears in his eyes. Cousin Mary had never seemed to be sorry because he wasn't like his father. She liked him just as he was.

Then Eugene forgot about his father. The ladies were getting ready to push their chairs back from the table.

"Wait, wait, Mrs. Brill!" he said.

"Eugene!" said his grandmother sharply. "What is wrong with you?"

"It's Mabel!" cried Eugene. "She's under Mrs. Brill's skirt."

"Who's Mabel?" asked Mrs. Deacon Ranney.

"She's Eugene's pet mouse," said Roswell happily, diving under the table.

Mrs. Brill jumped nimbly to a chair. She held her skirt above her high-topped shoes. Mrs. Deacon Ranney stayed on the floor, but she, too, lifted her skirt. She certainly could scream louder than any lady Eugene had ever heard. The boys could hardly believe that all this noise was being made in Grandmother's calm house.

Even Grandmother retreated to the kitchen door. This situation was much worse, Eugene thought, than the time Fuzzy got loose at the concert.

"You're scaring Mabel," Eugene said. "She isn't used to screaming."

"Shall we go into the parlor?" asked Grandmother calmly. She sounded as if she hadn't noticed the way her guests were acting.

"Eugene, take that beast away immediately. Take it outdoors and never, never bring an animal into this house again."

"But Mabel isn't used to living outdoors," Eugene protested.

Grandmother just looked steadily at him. Her look made it clear that Mabel would have to get used to living outdoors.

Mabel, frightened at the screaming, had found a place to hide. However, it didn't take long to find her after the ladies left. She was shivering in a corner of the dining room.

84

"Don't you think she looks pale, Eugene?" Roswell asked anxiously. "Do you suppose getting so frightened made her sick?"

Eugene held Mabel gently in his hands until she stopped shaking.

"What will you do with her?" Roswell asked.

"Well," Eugene said, "Grandmother didn't exactly say I couldn't keep her. She just said never to bring her into the house. Mabel didn't like it much here, anyway."

The boys were cheered by the thought that Mabel wouldn't need to be turned loose to take care of herself. They found a box in one corner of the old carriage house. They put some straw in one corner of the box.

Eugene put Mabel down in the straw. "Now don't go away, Mabel," he said. "We'll bring you something to eat after every meal." Mabel looked at Eugene with her beady black eyes. Then she started making a nest in the straw.

"Maybe she likes having her own house," Roswell said thoughtfully.

"Maybe she does," Eugene answered. But he was going to miss Mabel in his pocket.

The boys walked around to the front of the house and sat on the steps. Now Eugene had time to think about what Mrs. Ranney and Mrs. Brill had said at the dinner table. He'd never thought much about what he wanted to be when he grew up. Once in a while he had imagined he would probably be a lawyer like his father and his grandfather. But he wasn't like his father, and now he was sure he never could be.

While he was thinking, Eugene was watching a fuzzy yellow caterpillar on a rosebush. The caterpillar was certainly working hard to get to the top of the bush.

"A caterpillar wouldn't be a bad pet," he said thoughtfully. "It's soft and fuzzy, and I could carry it in my pocket."

86

"Grandmother said no more animals," Roswell reminded him. "She meant it, too."

"A caterpillar isn't an animal," Eugene said, "but Grandmother might think it is, so I'll keep him out of her way."

"You'd better keep him out of Mrs. Ranney's way. She certainly can scream. I've never heard any other lady scream as loud as Mrs. Ranney did. Just over a tiny little mouse, too. I don't see why she was afraid of Mabel."

But Eugene wasn't thinking about Mrs. Ranney. He was thinking that most words sounded the way they should. For instance, caterpillar sounded soft and fuzzy. Scream sounded loud and excited and frightened. He liked the sounds of words.

A Treasure House Discovered

"WHAT?" ASKED Eugene sleepily. He stirred uneasily in the big four-poster bed.

"Summer sun," something whispered softly.

Eugene sat up, wide awake now. Only Roswell, who was still asleep, was in the room with him. He looked out the window. It was a glorious day. He hoped it would be a better one than yesterday. He thought of all those stories about his father, but it was too nice a day to worry about anything.

"Summer sun," he heard again.

He slipped out of bed quietly so that Roswell wouldn't waken. He tiptoed to the window.

A long branch of the hickory tree brushed across the glass with a whispering sound.

"So that's what woke me. A breeze in the trees," Eugene whispered back to the strong wind outside, which was moving the branch. "That's a rhyme. I wonder if I could make up a whole poem. I think I could."

But he didn't have a chance to find out. His grandmother knocked at the door. "Time to get up, boys," she anounced. "It's a fine, sunny day. You must not waste it."

"Oo-ah," yawned Roswell, not at all sure he wanted to get up.

"Come, come," his grandmother called briskly. "it's too nice a day to waste."

"What are we going to do?" Roswell asked.

"I'd like to follow that little brook you told us about, Grandmother," Eugene said.

"If you promise not to go too far from the village, you may," Grandmother replied.

"Are there any fish in it?" Roswell asked.

"Yes, indeed," Mrs. Field answered. "Your grandfather often caught trout there."

"Some of Grandfather's fishing things are hanging in the shed," Eugene commented.

"So there are," agreed his grandmother cheerfully. "If you will be very careful of it, I will let you borrow his creel."

"What's a creel?" Roswell asked.

"It's a wicker basket to carry your fish home in," Grandmother explained.

"Oh, thank you, Grandmother," both boys shouted. "Thank you very much."

"You must not forget and leave it somewhere," she warned them.

"Oh, no, we won't," they promised eagerly.

Eugene's face clouded over. "What will we use for fishing poles?" he asked.

"You can buy two at Mr. Baine's store."

"But we haven't any money."

90

"Good gracious," their grandmother scolded. "Think boys! You have no money. You need money. What can you do to make money?"

"Work for it?" Eugene asked unhappily.

"Yes, indeed," his grandmother answered with crisp good humor.

"But where?" Eugene wanted to know.

"What can we do?" Roswell asked.

Their grandmother looked at them steadily for a moment. Eugene's blue eyes were sulky, and his blond hair hung limp on his forehead. Roswell watched Eugene, ready to do whatever his brother did.

"Lazy habits are easy to fall into," Grandmother warned. "Young as you are, you should be giving value for what you receive."

There was no response from the boys. Both of them looked decidedly unenthusiastic.

"Roswell, you may weed my flower garden, and I'll pay you enough for a fishing pole."

Eugene looked startled. Roswell had never paid any attention to flowers. He'd probably pull up all the day lilies and leave the dandelions. Eugene wished that grandmother had given him that job.

"Eugene, you may write me a sermon. You have been going to church almost every Sunday of your life. You must have some idea of what makes a good sermon. I'll expect a full page from you. It must be fair copy too, with no ink blots on the page."

Eugene's heart sank. He would much rather be out in the warm summer sunshine, working among the flowers. Now he would have to stay in the house. Besides, he had no idea what he could possibly write for a sermon.

Mrs. Field noticed Eugene's silence and the droop of his thin shoulders. She saw him glance despairingly out of the window. She thought she knew what was wrong. She smiled at him.

"You may sit on the porch in the sun while you write. I know you love the outdoors."

"Oh, Grandmother, thank you," he shouted happily. He ran to Mrs. Field and hugged her violently. She smoothed the limp hair back from his forehead gently.

"Remember, boys, I'll pay you enough for your fishing poles, but the work must be done well," she warned them.

"Yes, Grandmother," the boys nodded in agreement. Grandmother was strict but fair.

"Get dressed now and come down to breakfast," she told them. She rustled out of the door.

Eugene sat on the porch steps, chewing his ragged fingernails. Ideas came easily, but they just weren't sermon-type ideas. He twisted a lock of hair around and around.

The morning passed pleasantly. Roswell weeded slowly but carefully. "Aren't you through yet?" he asked Eugene at noon.

Eugene watched the graceful flight of an oriole until it was out of sight. Orioles were such gay creatures. What must it feel like to leave the earth behind? A low-slung brown dog trotted across the lawn. Did dogs mind not being able to fly?

"Eugene!" Roswell's impatient voice finally roused his brother.

"Oh—what did you say?" It was a question he asked often.

"Haven't you finished yet? We aren't going to have much time to fish."

"All right, I'll hurry." An impish gleam lighted Eugene's blue eyes.

Roswell smiled back at him. It was hard to stay cross with Eugene when he grinned like that. Roswell slumped down on the steps. He watched Eugene's slender fingers write.

"Whew, it's hot! Won't it cool us off to go wading? We'll have fun."

94

Eugene wrote a few last words. After all, writing wasn't so bad. It might even be fun. He stood up and stretched.

"Now are you finished?" Roswell asked.

"I'm through with what I've done."

"Is it what Grandmother wanted?" Roswell asked curiously. Eugene had written a few lines very fast, but the page wasn't covered.

"No." Eugene was sure of that.

"Bet you have to do it all over again, then," Roswell predicted darkly.

"We'll see." Eugene was pleased with what he had written. He felt too good to worry.

"Aren't you going to copy it?"

"No. You know I don't usually blot my papers or even cross out many words. I do wish I had some colored pencils, though, for the pictures around my poem."

"Your poem!" gasped Roswell. "Grandmother didn't tell you to write a poem."

"Poem!" echoed Mrs. Field as she came out on the porch. She read the four lines aloud.

> "Oh, had I wings like a dove I would fly
> Away from this world of fleas.
> I'd fly all around Miss Emerson's yard
> And light on Miss Emerson's trees.

"Eugene, is this your idea of a sermon?" she asked, looking at him severely.

"No, Grandmother, but I just didn't feel like writing a long, sad sermon. I felt like writing about Dooley. He's our dog at Amherst."

Mrs. Field shook her head disapprovingly. "Eugene, you must learn to be faithful in small things first. As you grow older, the habits you form as a child will go with you. No, for your own good, I cannot accept this poem about a dog. A dog is not an appropriate subject for a sermon. You must write a suitable sermon. After lunch you may try again."

96

After lunch the day didn't seem so carefree. The August sun was too hot. There was a stillness in the air. Roswell hurried to finish weeding the last clump of daisies.

Eugene took as his text the fifteenth verse of the thirteenth chapter of Proverbs. When he finally presented his sermon to his grandmother, she read it with interest.

"The life of a Christian is often compared to a race that is hard and to a battle in which a man must fight hard to win. These comparisons have prevented many from becoming Christians." Grandmother read this aloud, looking pleased. There was the hint of a smile at the corners of her eyes as she read the rest of it.

"That is a much better effort than your first one, young man," she said. "Go wash your face and hands, both of you. I will have your fishing pole money ready for you."

"Thank you, Grandmother," they shouted on

the way to their room. Soon the boys were racing down the front walk. The air was cooler now. The sun was hidden by a gray cloud. A crisp breeze was blowing.

Just as they reached the store, a few big drops of rain fell. By the time they had bought their poles, the rain was making patterns on the dusty road.

"There goes our fishing," Roswell wailed.

"Yes," agreed Eugene sadly.

A moment later he added, "We'll have lots of days to go fishing. Let's ask Grandmother if she will let us visit Grandfather's museum."

"All right, but I'd rather catch live fish than look at dead ones."

"Maybe we wouldn't have caught any, anyway," Eugene said. "I've wanted to see what's in that museum ever since we came."

After getting Grandmother's permission, the boys opened the door to the museum. It was dark inside, and Eugene left the door open so they could see better.

Insects were held by pins to boards and carefully labeled. Butterflies of all colors spread their wings across one wall. Birds' nests filled a table. In some of the nests there were eggs—spotted, speckled, mottled and plain. Ferns and leaves had been pressed and dried and then mounted. All parts of the exhibits were neatly named.

"There's nothing here but old eggs and dried-up butterflies," Roswell complained. "In the Amherst Museum there's a big gorilla taller than a man. Now that's something to see."

Eugene didn't even hear his brother. He was too busy looking at the Latin names on the labels under the butterflies.

"Oh, Rozy," he called later. "Look here!"

"I don't see anything but a lot of old stones. I can look at stones anywhere."

"Yes, but there are so many different kinds. See how these sparkle!" Eugene held up a dark gray stone that caught and held the light.

"I thought I heard Grandmother call," Roswell said, going to the door.

"I didn't," Eugene replied crossly.

"How could you hear anything when your head's half way down a barrel?" Roswell asked.

"It is Grandmother calling! Come on!" Roswell ran out of the museum.

The third time there could be no mistake. It was Grandmother calling. Eugene carefully closed the door behind him and ran to the house. Grandmother stood in the doorway.

"I'm sorry, Grandmother," he panted. "I didn't hear you. I was trying to see all the things in the museum."

"Roswell told me you were interested in your grandfather's collections. The museum is an interesting place, is it not?"

101

"Oh, yes, Grandmother!" Eugene glanced hastily at the erect old lady. How gentle her voice was. She wasn't cross with him for being late this time. Did she, too, like to collect things? Or was it that the museum reminded her of Grandfather and her own sons?

"Supper's ready. Wash, please, Eugene. Your hands and face are very dirty."

Racing upstairs to get ready for supper, Eugene was doubly happy. He had somehow missed a scolding for being late, and he had discovered a treasure house.

A Surprise for Cousin Mary

EUGENE WAS glad to be back in Amherst. He knew he would never forget his visit to Vermont, though. Next to Grandfather's museum he had loved the woods, with their damp forest smell, best of all. Ferns grew everywhere. They hung over the rocks and grew along the edges of the stream where he and Roswell fished for trout. Grandmother told the boys that more than eighty kinds of ferns grew in Vermont.

Eugene and Roswell had enjoyed picking the tiny, sweet wild strawberries. They had also spent hours trying to make friends with the woodchucks, toads, and other creatures which lived in the woods. They had found many of these animals easy to tame.

Eugene had collected a little bit of everything. Then he compared the things he had found with the things in Grandfather's museum. He brought his treasures back to Amherst in a dusty cardboard box.

"You surely don't intend to keep those dead butterflies and dirty rocks," Lizzie had said, looking at them in dismay.

"They're collections," Eugene had insisted. He was glad Lizzie hadn't noticed the beetles.

"Perhaps you should collect just one thing," Cousin Mary had suggested.

"But I'm interested in all of these things," Eugene had answered.

Finally it was agreed that he might collect what he liked, but that he must keep the whole collection in boxes so Lizzie wouldn't have to dust it. Grandmother had been right when she told him it would be better not to try to collect snakes. He tried to imagine Lizzie dusting a stuffed snake.

Grandmother approved of his collections. He guessed it was because his grandfather had liked to collect things too. He'd been right, when he guessed that he would never suit Grandmother in most ways. He just couldn't be very much like his father.

Now it was winter. Of course there were lessons and chores like bringing in the wood. For fun there was sledding, sleigh riding, and taffy pulls. It was a cold winter, and it seemed to Eugene and Roswell that they were in the house too much. Cousin Mary, Aunt Mary, and Lizzie thought so, too.

Often the boys were sent on errands to one house or another. They might be sent to Miss Dickinson's with some chicken soup for her sister Emily, who was ill. Or they might be sent to the Mitchells' house with a note inviting them to supper. The boys enjoyed doing these errands. They were almost always invited inside to get warm by the stove and to eat whatever was being cooked. They learned that Mrs. Mitchell always baked spicy ginger cookies on Saturdays. They also learned many other things, because everyone told them the news at each house. They, in turn, passed on the news at the other houses they visited.

"Next week Eliza Bratten's going to Boston to study singing," Eugene remarked, biting into his warm brown cooky.

"But her father says that she'll have to come home if she can't learn to sing in six months," Roswell added. He always took tiny bites to make his cooky last a long time. Eugene ate his fast in case he was offered another one.

"Land sakes," said Mrs. Mitchell, sliding another pan of cookies into the oven. "You boys are better than a newspaper. Have another cooky, Eugene. I see, Roswell, you haven't finished yours yet."

As the boys plowed their way through the snow on the way home, Roswell asked, "What makes you so quiet, Eugene? You haven't said a word all the way."

"Something Mrs. Mitchell said gave me an idea," Eugene said. "I'll tell you about it, but let's surprise Cousin Mary."

During the next week the boys were unusually busy. When they were sent on an errand they were often gone a long time. They also spent a great deal of time in their room.

Saturday morning after breakfast Eugene handed Cousin Mary a piece of paper rolled up like a scroll. The paper was quite wide, and it was tied with a rather dirty blue ribbon.

"I have a present for you, Cousin Mary," he said proudly.

"A present?" said Aunt Mary. "How nice! What in the world could it be?"

"It's the first issue of our newspaper," said Eugene. His eyes were shining. "Mrs. Mitchell said Roswell and I were as good as a newspaper, so I decided we could really write one. Read it, Cousin Mary. Read it out loud so Aunt Mary and Lizzie can hear."

"A newspaper," said Cousin Mary, smiling. "What a nice idea." She untied the ribbon and unrolled the paper.

"The Amherst Chronicle, Issue Number I," she read. "Amherst is very quiet this month. There is so much snow the horses' hooves hardly make any noise at all. It is so cold that mostly only the men and boys go outdoors. The ladies stay inside and tell the men and boys to wipe off their feet when they come in."

Cousin Mary smiled. "Very descriptive, dear," she said. "Very well written."

"That isn't the best part," Roswell said.

Aunt Mary went on reading. "Some places it isn't so quiet, though. Down at the livery stable Lije Elliot and Mr. Dudley Waite got in an argument about whether Abraham Lincoln would win the election or not. Mr. Dudley Waite hit Lije Elliot, which made his nose bleed all over his new waistcoat. Several gentlemen who were there thought there would be a nice fight. But just then Mrs. Dudley Waite came to see what had happened to Mr. Dudley Waite and made him go home."

"Dear me," Aunt Mary said.

"You know you're not supposed to go near the livery stable," said Lizzie.

The boys smiled proudly as Cousin Mary read on. "Eliza Bratten's been in Boston for several weeks now, and her father says she can't sing any better than she could when she left, so it looks as if she'll be home soon."

"Forevermore," said Lizzie. Her shoulders were shaking with laughter.

Cousin Mary read to the bottom of the page. Aunt Mary said "Dear me," and Lizzie said "Forevermore" after nearly every item.

"Do you like it?" Roswell asked anxiously.

"How many copies shall we make?" asked Eugene. "I thing people will want to read it."

Cousin Mary looked at them for a moment without saying anything.

Eugene was worried. "Didn't you think it was interesting?" he asked. "Don't you think it would make people laugh?"

"It was very interesting indeed," Cousin Mary said. "But did you stop to think how the people you've written about will feel when they read what you have to say about them? Surely Mr. Waite is sorry he was so rude, and Mrs. Waite would be embarrassed to have her friends read about the incident. I'm sure Eliza Bratten has

111

been studying very hard in Boston. How will she feel when she reads that her father says she doesn't sing well?"

"I didn't think about that," Eugene said. "I only wanted to make it interesting."

He took the paper from Aunt Mary's hand and tore it into several pieces.

"Oh, Eugene," said Roswell, "how can you tear up our newspaper after we worked so hard to get the news and then write all of it?"

"We don't want to hurt anyone's feelings," Eugene said. "Besides, we had a lot of fun writing our newspaper."

He was surprised to realize that his statement was really true. It had been fun trying to find just the right words to use in the newspaper, even if nobody ever saw them.

Goat in the Lion's Den

Eugene Field's blue eyes looked fiercely at the six boys and three girls. They were sitting in the hayloft of the Boltwoods' big barn. It was 1862, and the War Between the States was still dragging on.

"I say we should help our Union soldiers," Eugene said loudly.

"Of course we should," the others agreed.

"But how can we help?" Adelina asked. She tossed her long golden curls back over her shoulder. She knew Mary and Sarah were wishing their straight black braids would turn into bright curls like hers overnight.

"The Ladies' Benevolent Society makes bandages for the soldiers," Robert said. "I tried to help Mother make some, but she had to do them all over again and was cross."

"I didn't mean for us to do anything like that," Eugene explained. "I think we should raise some money for our Union soldiers."

"Money?" the children echoed. Doubtfully the group looked at each other. None of them ever had much spending money. Since the war had begun, they had had even less than before.

"Yes," Eugene insisted. "I have a plan."

"What is your plan?" asked Robert.

"We can give a play," Eugene replied.

"Let's do it," the others cried.

"How will our giving a play help the soldiers?" Adelina asked. "The soldiers won't be around here so that they can see it."

"We can charge admission. Whatever we take in, we can give to the soldiers."

"We always charge admission when we give a play. But what good will two pins a person do? Soldiers don't especially need pins, do they?" Adelina wasn't convinced.

Eugene laughed with the others. "We'll collect money instead of pins," he explained. "Of course we'll invite our families. Then we can use the money to buy the things the soldiers need. Cousin Mary says the army needs blankets and shoes and other things. She says money is needed to help slaves escape, too."

Twelve-year-old Eugene looked so eager that the small group, as usual, decided to do as he suggested. Helping slaves escape sounded scary and exciting and patriotic all at the same time. The idea appealed to all of them.

"What play shall we give?" asked Joseph.

"How about Abraham and Lot?" asked Mary.

"There aren't enough parts for all of us in that one," Robert protested.

115

"What about David and Jonathan? We could use spearmen and bowmen and servants."

"There are only three good parts in that one," Robert didn't want to be a spearman.

"Let's give Moses and the Israelites crossing the Red Sea," John suggested.

"No, indeed," answered a Boltwood boy. "Mother said we couldn't bring any more water into the barn. Remember what happened when we played Noah's Ark in here?"

Everyone was quiet. All the boys and girls remembered quite clearly what had happened when they had played with water. It had taken the hay a long, long time to dry out.

"We need something exciting," Eugene said thoughtfully. "It ought to be something like Daniel in the Lion's Den."

The children were all pleased at this idea. They made several suggestions.

"There's King Darius—and a Queen."

116

"And four evil princes."

"Who will write the play?" asked Nathan, already knowing the answer.

"Eugene, of course," the others said.

"Will you, Eugene?" asked Adelina. "Will there be a good part for me?"

"Yes, I'll write the play. And where there's a King, there has to be a Queen."

Adelina brushed a wisp of hay off her long golden curls. She turned to Mary and Sarah. "You may be my handmaidens," she said kindly, feeling sorry for them because they never were chosen for the best parts.

"Well, really——" Mary began.

"On second thought," Eugene interrupted, laughing at their expressions, "maybe the Queen should have dark straight hair."

"Oh, Eugene! You're such a tease!" all three girls groaned.

Eugene's eyes were sparkling with fun. He

loved to tease Adelina. She was always so sure the best part in the plays they gave would go to her. Somehow, she usually was cast as the princess or the damsel in distress, but Eugene didn't make it easy for her.

"I'm going to be King Darius," the oldest Boltwood boy said. "I'll use my father's goldheaded walking stick as a sceptre."

"All right," Eugene agreed. "You're the biggest, anyway."

"Let Rozy be Daniel," said Mary. "He's always good about learning his lines."

Roswell smiled. He usually got things done. It was nice to be liked, too.

"That leaves Joseph, Nathan, Robert and me for the four evil princes," Eugene said.

"What about the lion?" asked Sarah.

"I've already thought about that," Eugene admitted. "We'll use William, our goat."

"How can a goat be a lion?" asked Sarah.

118

"That's easy. We'll just gather lots of those fuzzly ferns. Fuzzly ferns—those words together sound ticklish. They almost make me want to sneeze. I like them."

The children waited patiently. Eugene often stopped what he was doing to say something with a funny sound over and over again.

"We'll gather armloads of the curly-leaved ferns from the woods," he continued. "Then when they're dry and brown, we can make a big mane for the lion."

"What about William's horns?" Adelina said critically. "Lions don't have horns."

"Oh, didn't you know about his horns?" Roswell asked. "Cousin Mary had them cut off the last time he butted Lizzie. I don't think he likes Lizzie very much."

"How soon can you have the play written, Eugene?" Joseph asked.

"I'll have it done by next Saturday," Eugene

promised. "My father is coming for a visit, and I'll want to have it finished."

"Can we surprise him?" pleaded Roswell.

"Maybe," Eugene smiled at his brother.

Just then the big brass bell at the Boltwood back door clanged twice.

"That's for us," the Boltwood boys said. They raced for the house. It was suppertime, and it didn't pay to be late.

"There's plenty of space on the threshing floor to put chairs for the grown people and benches for the children," Eugene said, after all of them had climbed down from the ladder.

The next week when the children met again, Eugene brought the promised play. It wasn't long, but it was exciting. Eugene read well, and he read it to the assembled children.

The boys and girls were eager to begin learning their parts. Adelina had won the Queen's part because her mother had a golden tiara that

she could wear for a crown. The barn buzzed with their happy noise.

Roswell had borrowed Cousin Mary's best brocade bathrobe. Robert was to wear a pair of real Chinese slippers. Mary and Sarah had promised to take good care of a pair of Japanese fans to keep the queen cool. Silk scarves had been begged for turbans. Rugs for the King's court had been loaned to them.

They made plans to borrow chairs. They decided where to place benches.

"What about lights?" Eugene asked.

"My father says something always happens when you are in charge, Eugene," one Boltwood boy said. "He says 'absolutely no lanterns!' "

"We probably won't need them anyway," the children decided. "The summer sun will still be bright when we have the play."

When the night of the play finally came, Mr. Field was sitting in Cousin Mary's parlor. The chicken dinner had been delicious, and he was in a mellow mood. The boys had behaved very well. He had been right, he decided, to bring them to his sister.

"Father, here is something for you," Eugene said. He felt rather shy. He had not seen his father in a long time.

"Read it, please, Father," Roswell begged.

"Is this an invitation to the play Cousin Mary told me about?" Mr. Field asked.

"It's a formal invitation, Father," Eugene said. "We want you to come."

"The Amherst Players
invite you to attend an
Evening Entertainment
in the
Boltwood Barn at 7 P.M.
Proceeds for the War Fund"

Mr. Field read. "I was hoping to see the play," he continued, "since Eugene wrote it and both of you boys are in it."

"Oh, we are," Roswell said excitedly. "I'm to be Daniel. Eugene is to be one of the evil princes, and he wrote the whole play."

"Slow down, son," Mr. Field said, laughing. "Is everyone invited?"

"Yes, sir. Cousin Mary and Aunt Mary and you and Lizzie, too, if she wants to come."

Lizzie, hearing her name, came into the room. "What's the trouble now?" she asked.

"No trouble, Lizzie," said Mr. Field soothingly. "Neighborhood children have invited us to a play this evening in Boltwood's barn."

"I'm not likely to be going with a company dinner to wash up after," Lizzie snorted.

Eugene and Roswell exchanged a happy look. Then they heard Cousin Mary say, "Just leave things as they are, Lizzie. This should be worth seeing if only for the costumes. The boys have been borrowing silk scarves, jewelry, velvet robes, and even one of our rugs."

124

The two boys held their breaths. To their intense relief, Lizzie objected. "No, Miss Mary, if I leave this chicken gravy and the mashed potatoes on the plates until morning, they'll stick like glue."

Roswell grinned at his brother. Then, to their horror, Mr. Field interrupted. Whenever he insisted, things were done his way.

"Now Lizzie," he said in his deep voice, "you really must come with us."

Lizzie looked at him sharply. She didn't like to be laughed at.

"We just won't go without you," he declared.

"Very well, I'll come with you. But mind you, I'll be thinking of my dirty dishes all the evening," Lizzie said pointedly.

The boys glanced at each other dismally. They had been certain that Lizzie would refuse to go. William the goat butted her whenever he saw her. Besides, they didn't want William distracted during the play. At rehearsals he had behaved quite well. If Lizzie attracted his attention, what would happen?

"I hope she sits far back in the audience and that there are lots of people in front of her," Eugene said without much hope.

But Lizzie sat in the front row. "If I'm going, I'm going to see," she declared.

There was a good crowd. Eugene was glad to see the barn was quite filled and all the chairs and benches taken. The children should be able to buy several blankets for the soldiers. Maybe there would even be enough money to give some to the "conductors" on the Underground Railway. Eugene knew those people always needed money to carry on their work.

A nagging worry followed Eugene backstage. Being an actor, a stage manager, and an animal trainer all at once was hard, he decided. He couldn't be in three places at once.

The first act of the play went smoothly. The audience clapped loudly and cheered as the young actors bowed and left the stage.

In the second act, William was not a success as a lion. He looked exactly like a goat with dried ferns around his neck.

First, the audience laughed at poor William as he stood blinking in the sun. Then the people roared happily as the ferns tickled his nose and he sneezed. The laughter grew louder as he lowered his head, stiffened his legs, and refused to move offstage with Roswell.

It was at this moment that Lizzie said very loudly, "Humph, I told them that ornery goat wouldn't do anything they wanted him to!"

At the sound of Lizzie's rasping voice, William looked up. When he saw Lizzie he pulled away from Roswell. With one long leap he was off the stage. With lowered head he butted Lizzie's knees with all his might.

Over backward went Lizzie's chair. Up in the air went Lizzie's large feet. Mr. Field rushed to help her stand up. After finding out that she was not seriously hurt, he suggested, "Perhaps it would be best if you went back to the house to lie down for a while."

"Likely I'll never get up again," Lizzie said darkly. "Knew I ought to wash those dishes and not come to this play."

Everyone was laughing and talking loudly now. Eugene knew the children couldn't finish the play. He had worked hard to make this occasion a success, but he was sure his father would scold him when the family returned home.

Oddly enough, Mr. Field didn't scold the boys. He felt sorry because they hadn't been able to go on. He was amused at the goat and went over to comfort Eugene.

"Don't worry, Eugene," he said kindly. "All of us make mistakes. It's how you learn from them that matters. Next time you'll know that there are certain dangers in using a goat for one of your actors."

"I've learned never to let William within sight of Lizzie again," Eugene said.

"It was a good play as far as it went. How much money did you collect?"

Eugene's eyes brightened. "Quite a bit, really, Father. Several of the men said the play was for a worthy cause and gave a whole dollar. Others gave a little extra. I think we took in almost ten dollars."

"And a plugged nickel," Roswell added.

"Now it's not only the grown people who are winning the war, is it, Father?"

Mr. Field looked at his boys proudly. "No, indeed. Whenever the children try to help win the war, it's bound to end soon."

Eugene began to hear people talking. "Imagine a goat taking a lion's part!"

"He managed to steal the lion's share of attention, at least!"

"A goat on the stage!"

"What were those children thinking of?"

"That's the main trouble today. Children just don't think about what might happen!"

"Those poor Field boys. In trouble again!"

"They're always in trouble!"

Eugene turned back to the stage. There were costumes to be returned.

It had been a good idea. William had behaved nicely at rehearsals, too. If Lizzie had just stayed home! He smiled as he remembered how Lizzie's feet had flown up in the air. She really had looked surprised as she fell over backwards. She would be very angry.

Eugene decided he would have to be especially nice to her for a week or so. However, he had no doubt that she would forgive him sooner or later. She always did.

Eugene Helps Again

"Keep turning the crank, Eugene," said Lizzie. "The ice cream will never be ready by the time the ladies are through if you don't use a little more elbow grease."

"Did you ever wonder how elbow grease got its name, Lizzie?" Eugene asked.

"Good land, no," said Lizzie. "The things you find to worry about! Just keep on turning that crank, and don't talk so much."

Eugene turned the crank on the big ice cream freezer a little faster. The back porch was hot. His shirt was plastered to his back. Rivers of perspiration ran down his face.

131

"Why does the Ladies' Benevolent Society have to meet on a hot day like this instead of a cool day?" he complained.

"Shame on you, Eugene Field," Lizzie said. She stood in the kitchen doorway, fanning herself with her apron. "The war goes on all the time, whether it's hot or not. I don't know how our soldiers would get along if everyone made bandages or sewed for them only on nice days. I suppose you think our soldiers fight only on cool days!"

Roswell ran around the corner of the house. "I'll take a turn! I'll take a turn!" His job had been to open the door for the ladies. He was bored.

Eugene went on turning the crank. Roswell worked better at things he had to beg to do.

"I don't know, Rozy," he said. "This old freezer turns pretty hard."

"Oh, please let me help," Roswell pleaded.

"I'm big and strong. I can do it. Let me try. I'll show you I can do it."

"Well, all right." Eugene gave the crank a few more turns. He didn't want to seem too anxious. "But I don't think you can do it."

Roswell sat down on the back steps by the freezer. "Thank you, Eugene," he said, and he took over the tiresome task.

"Oh, that's all right, Roswell," said Eugene kindly. Then he started toward the shade of the big elm tree in the back yard.

"Just a minute, Eugene Field!" Lizzie called. "I don't know how you got Roswell to take over that job, but there's plenty of work for all. March yourself into the kitchen."

The back porch had been cool compared to the steaming kitchen. That morning Lizzie had baked little cakes in the big black stove. They were all frosted with pink icing and ready on a big ironstone platter.

"Couldn't I have just one, Lizzie?" Eugene begged. "I'm so hungry after all that work I might fall dead here on the floor."

"That's a chance we'll just have to take," Lizzie said. "No cakes for you until all this silver is cleaned. There are two cakes each for you and Roswell. The ones on the platter are all counted, so don't get any ideas!"

"Why, Lizzie," said Eugene, "you sound as if you thought I might take one."

They both laughed. They were remembering the blueberry pie.

"Those ladies would have to be jugglers to use all this silver," Eugene complained.

"Might as well do it all while you're doing it," Lizzie said.

The kitchen was quiet for a while. There was no noise but the swish of Lizzie's dishwater and the clinking of the silver. Eugene could hear scraps of conversation from the dining room. Then he became interested.

"The war might last for years," Mrs. Mitchell was saying. "The South is fighting hard."

"My husband says the generals make too many mistakes," another lady said.

When all the silver was polished, Eugene slipped into one corner of the dining room. He hated this War Between the States. Most of the young men from Amherst had joined the army. Some of them, he knew, would never come back. He hadn't thought before that the war might really last for years. He wanted to hear what the ladies were saying.

"It's hard for me to eat," Mrs. Warren said, "knowing that Johnny might be hungry."

"I think our soldiers have enough to eat," another lady said. "It's just that what they have is not very good."

"Johnny was always such a one for cake," Mrs. Warren said. "I wonder how long it will be before he has another piece."

Eugene went back to the kitchen. The ice cream was now hard. Lizzie covered the freeezr with an old rug so the ice cream would not melt before the ladies were ready for it.

Roswell's face was red and his hair was wet. "I finished it," he said proudly. "Next time, though, I don't think I will. You were right. That old freezer does turn hard."

Eugene did not answer. He was thinking of something else. "Lizzie," he asked, "where do the bandages go?"

"Why, they might go anyplace," Lizzie answered. "Goodness knows there are plenty of places where they're needed. They might even go to some battlefield where Miss Clara Barton is. That woman is a real saint. Her nursing has saved a good many lives."

Lizzie went into the dining room.

"These are our cakes on this blue plate," Roswell said. "Let's go out in the yard and eat them. I'm hungry."

Eugene was thinking about Johnny Warren. The Warrens were good friends of Cousin Mary, and Johnny had been kind to Eugene and Roswell. Once he had taken them to Clay Island to hunt for the oddly shaped stones along the shore. Another time he had taken them to the hotel and paid five cents apiece for glasses of lemonade with straws. The boys had never had lemonade that cost five cents a glass before. Somehow it tasted better than the kind poured from a pitcher at home.

"Roswell," Eugene said, "I'd like to talk to you about those cakes.

Roswell's eyes grew bigger as he listened to Eugene. Then he nodded. In a few minutes Lizzie came back into the kitchen.

"They're ready for their ice cream now," she said. "Spread those bowls out on the table. Carry them into the dining room as fast as I get them filled."

The boys carried dishes of the rich vanilla ice cream to the dining room until they had served everyone. Then Lizzie filled huge bowls for the

138

boys. They spooned it is as if they would never have any more ice cream.

"Land sakes," Lizzie said. "How can you eat so much ice cream when you've already had two cakes apiece?"

"Oh," Roswell said, "we didn't——" But Eugene frowned at him.

"Didn't what?" asked Lizzie.

"Didn't feel too full," Eugene answered.

After supper that night everyone sat on the front porch. There was still no breeze stirring. Aunt Mary rocked back and forth in the big squeaky chair. Lizzie fanned herself briskly with a bamboo fan. Cousin Mary sat on the top step with the two boys, watching the stars and listening to the chirping of the katydids. They were pleasantly tired and content because of a job well done.

"The cakes were especially good this afternoon, Lizzie," she said. "Several of the ladies said they were delicious. Didn't you think the cakes were good, boys?"

"Oh, we didn't have any," Roswell answered before Eugene could stop him.

"Didn't have any indeed!" Lizzie snapped. "Then what became of the four cakes I left on the blue plate for you boys?"

"We decided to send them to Johnny Warren," Roswell answered. "He doesn't get any cake. He needed it worse than we did."

"Just how do you plan to do that, pray tell?" Lizzie asked.

"Well," Eugene answered, "We asked where the bandages were going, and you said they might go anyplace, so we thought——"

"Oh, Eugene, you didn't put those cakes in the box with the bandages!" Cousin Mary exclaimed, jumping to her feet.

"Don't worry, Cousin Mary," Roswell said. "We wrapped them up nicely."

140

Cousin Mary hurried into the dining room and the boys followed. She knelt on the floor beside the big brown box in which the bandages had been packed. She tried to remove the top layer, but many of the bandages were stuck together with what looked like pink glue. When the soggy pink bandages were finally pried loose, they could see a mixture of sticky newspaper, cake crumbs, and pink frosting. They looked at the mess in dismay.

"Eugene Field!" Cousin Mary began angrily. "How could you!" Then she picked a small piece of paper out of the box. "To Whom It May Concern," she read. "We really don't need this cake. If Johnny Warren is there, give it to him. If not give it to anybody who hasn't had cake for a long time. Yours very truly, Eugene and Roswell Field."

Cousin Mary looked into Eugene's disappointed blue eyes. She sighed.

"I guess only one layer of bandages has been spoiled," she said, "and your intentions were kind. But Eugene, I do think the war would be over sooner if you wouldn't try to help."

Eugene went out under the elm trees to think things over, and his brother followed him. In his imagination he could always plan things and see certain results. Somehow, when he tried out his ideas, they didn't work out successfully. Why didn't anything ever work out the way he expected it to in the beginning?

A Short Ride and a Long Walk

"ARE YOU SURE this boat is strong enough to go over the dam?" Roswell asked anxiously.

"Of course it'll go over," Eugene answered impatiently. "Why wouldn't it?"

"I know it'll go over. What I meant was, will it go over without coming apart?"

"Look here, Rozy," said Eugene, "we built this boat ourselves, and we know it's a good one. It may not look fancy, but it's strong. When we asked Mr. Tufts if we could make a boat out of the old wood by the pond, he said it was all right. Do you think he'd say it was all right if he thought we were going to drown ourselves in it?

143

This boat's perfectly safe. Stop worrying about it, and let's get going."

"We didn't tell him we were going over the dam in it," Roswell said. He looked at the big house on the hill. Some of its windows overlooked the quiet mill pond on which they were rowing. "We didn't even tell him we were going to row on the pond in the boat. If he sees us he'll probably run out and stop us," Roswell said hopefully.

"He and Mrs. Tufts are having tea on the other side of the house," said Eugene. "This is our last day before everyone else comes to school. After that, we probably won't get much time to row. It will be study, study, study."

Eugene was still not happy that Cousin Mary and their father had decided to send them to the Reverend Mr. Tuft's school.

"You'll like it," Cousin Mary had said. "There will be six other boys there, and you'll live in the

Tuft's big house. It will be just like a big family."

"We like it here," Eugene said. "We don't want to be like a big family. There are enough people right in this house."

"It will be good for you," Cousin Mary had said firmly. "You will learn to study."

Eugene had said nothing more. When Cousin Mary decided something was good for them, they might just as well give up.

So far, it was hard to tell what school would be like. They had arrived several days before the other pupils. The Reverend Mr. Tufts had not asked much of them except that they stay out in the fresh air and come to meals on time with clean hands. Mrs. Tufts was a pretty, kind lady who reminded them of Aunt Mary. The Tufts' house was big and rambling. In back of it were beautiful wooded hills, which the boys enjoyed exploring. They had spent much of their time wandering over these hills.

The boat project had been Eugene's idea. What they had built was really more like a raft, but it floated. Roswell enjoyed just rowing around on the quiet pond, but Eugene wanted to know what would happen if they rowed over the dam which flowed into the stream below.

"It would be fun," he said.

Now they had rowed closer to the dam. It dropped almost straight down, and at the bottom the water churned into a white foam.

"Let's don't," Roswell said. Even Eugene did not like the way the water boiled up. It looked as if there might be rocks down there. He thought perhaps they ought to find the safest place to go over before they tried it.

But it was too late. Suddenly the boat was swept into the current. Eugene and Roswell screamed as the raft shot over the dam and hit the bottom with a splintering crash. The stream seemed full of boards and boys. The water was icy cold, but it was not deep. Soon both boys were shivering on the bank. Mr. and Mrs. Tufts came running from the house.

Mrs. Tufts was wringing her hands. "They might have drowned," she said.

"It is unlikely that they would have drowned in eight inches of water," Mr. Tufts answered. "However, I am distressed at their lack of thought. Why did you not examine the dam and the stream first to see what would probably happen when the boat went over?"

"We didn't think," said Eugene meekly. His teeth were chattering.

"That's it exactly," said Mr. Tufts. "You didn't think, and you need to think."

"Perhaps it would be better if they thought upstairs in their room with some warm blankets over them," Mrs. Tufts suggested.

When the boys were settled in their beds in their flannel pajamas, Mrs. Tufts covered them with two quilts apiece. She put hot bricks wrapped in flannel by their feet. She also made them drink some hot herb tea, which tasted rather awful.

"Eugene," said Roswell after Mrs. Tufts had left the room, "what did you think about when the boat came apart?"

"I was too scared to think at all then," Eugene answered. "But when we were standing on the bank, I was trying to think what kind of noise the water was making. It wasn't what you'd call splashing. I'd say it was something like rumbling, only more watery."

"What a silly thing to think about," Roswell said sleepily. "I was thinking how cold the water was, and how cross Aunt Mary would be if she knew I had my good shoes on. Do you think we can go downstairs for dinner?"

"I don't know," said Eugene. "Mr. Tufts told us we had to stay up here and think."

Roswell soon went to sleep, but Eugene stayed awake. He was thinking, but probably not about what Mr. Tufts had intended him to think about. What word would you use to describe the sound of that water, anyway? Gurgling? Rippling? Swashing? None of them seemed exactly right. But Eugene knew the right word was always waiting if you could only find it.

The week after the boys' boat ride was busy. The other boys arrived, and Mr. Tufts began his school. Eugene and Roswell were not used to studying the same things at the same time every day. Mr. Tufts seemed to feel that there were many things they should have learned which they did not know. When one of them gave the wrong answer, Mr. Tufts would look at him and say, "Think, boy, think!"

"I am thinking," Eugene would sometimes reply. He was thinking, too, but usually not about arithmetic or history or geography. He did like Latin though. In fact, he did so well that Mr. Tufts suggested that he try writing letters to his father in Latin. Eugene enjoyed doing this. He was sure it was something which would make his father proud of him.

In spite of Latin, and in spite of the fact that he liked Mr. and Mrs. Tufts, Eugene was homesick. He longed to see Cousin Mary and Aunt Mary and Lizzie. He wanted to get up in the morning and wonder what he would do that day. He was tired of knowing when he woke up that he would be expected to be in his place at the breakfast table at exactly seven o'clock and that at eight o'clock his algebra lesson would begin. He hated algebra anyway.

He was tired of just being in the house with so many people. He'd like to spend just one afternoon curled up by the fire in Aunt Mary's parlor with a book in his lap and a juicy apple in his hand. He wrote Aunt Mary that he would like to come home. She wrote back, "Nonsense. You are very fortunate to be in such a fine school. You will soon become quite used to it, and will like it so well you will not want to come home at all."

The day after Cousin Mary's letter came Eugene woke Roswell before daylight. Roswell was usually half-dressed before he really woke up. He swung his legs over the edge of the bed and rubbed his eyes.

"It's dark this morning," he said. "Are you sure it's time to get up?"

"Listen, Rozy," Eugene said in a whisper, "I don't want to stay here any longer, so I've decided we'll go home today. Hurry up and dress, while everybody's still asleep."

Roswell's mouth hung open. "Are you crazy, Eugene?" he asked. "How do you expect to get home? It's twenty-five miles away."

"It won't be hard," Eugene answered. "The

railroad goes through the village. All we have to do is follow the tracks. Twenty-five miles isn't so far to walk. Hurry up and get dressed before anyone else gets up. I've already been to the kitchen and fixed bread and butter and apples for us to eat along the way."

Roswell looked at his tall, thin brother, but he tried not to look into his blue eyes. Somehow Eugene had a way of getting people to do what he wanted when they looked into his eyes. "I'm not going," he said firmly.

"Not going?" Eugene asked in surprise. It was the first time Roswell had ever refused to follow his brother.

"Cousin Mary will be angry, and Mr. Tufts will be angry. Besides, I like it here." Roswell climbed back into bed.

Eugene looked at his own warm bed and then at the darkness outside the window. Then he turned and went out the door, awkwardly hold-

ing his package of lunch. "Well, good-by, Roswell," he said slowly.

Eugene counted five thousand railroad ties before the sun was very high in the sky, but he knew he was still a long way from Amherst. Before noon he was sitting down every few ties to rest. His feet felt as if they were the size of an elephant's feet, and they hurt all over. He tried taking off his shoes, but it was a chilly day. When he put the shoes back on, his feet felt worse than ever.

The lunch he had thought would be enough for both him and Roswell was gone long before he was halfway to Amherst. He was hungry, as well as cold and exhausted all afternoon.

It was dark when Eugene finally stumbled up Aunt Mary's front walk. The lamp had been lighted in the parlor. He could see Cousin Mary and Aunt Mary sitting by the fire. He was so tired he could hardly lift the brass knocker.

Lizzie came to the door, holding a lamp. She peered down at him.

"Forevermore!" she said, as if she had seen a ghost. "Forevermore! It's Eugene!"

The family sat by the fire while Eugene told about his long walk. Aunt Mary fussed over him. She took off his shoes and rubbed his feet. She kept saying, "Poor boy."

Lizzie clucked her tongue and shook her head after nearly every sentence. Cousin Mary said nothing at all until he had told the whole story. Then she said, "You'd better get to bed, Eugene. You'll have to get up early, because your train leaves at eight o'clock in the morning."

"Mary, you're surely not going to send that poor boy back in the morning after the terrible day he had getting home," fussed Aunt Mary. Even Lizzie looked surprised.

"Eugene knows he did the wrong thing," Cousin Mary said. "One of the reasons he was sent away to school was to learn to act more responsibly. He has worried Mr. Tufts, and he has worried us. As you say, he had a terrible day. All this was because he selfishly did not consider the results of his actions."

Eugene knew she was right. He would have to go back to school, but he knew he would never really like it. Wasn't there any place in the world for a person who didn't like doing the same things every day?

Castle in the Woods

"Roswell, i am in sore need of more branches."

A tall, slim fifteen-year-old boy stood at the side of a deep ditch. Beyond him, the ditch was covered with leaves, sticks, and brushwood. No one would expect to find a trench underneath the branches.

"By my good sword, Eugene, you do work with a will," Roswell called back loudly. "Aren't all the branches used already?"

"Yes, indeed, brother," came the answer.

"Then come to us and help cut some of these beech boughs. Ernest and James are well worn, and my shirt sticks to my back."

"And leave yon castle unguarded? Nay, ask not that," Eugene replied. He was by now resting comfortably on a fallen log. He smiled happily. It had taken the boys a long time to dig this moat. His job of covering it over to hide it was easier by far than sawing tree branches. He did not want to change jobs now.

The four boys had read tales of castles and knights all summer. It was Eugene who had discovered these exciting books.

They had decided to build a castle off in the deep woods. They liked to go there when school became too difficult. Mr. Tufts was not often cross with them, but Latin and Greek were not much fun. Sunny afternoons usually found the boys working on their castle in the cool forest. They kept thinking of ways to change and improve it.

In olden times each castle had been surrounded by a deep ditch filled with water. This was called a moat. People in the castle were safe because no one could cross this moat unless the drawbridge was down.

The boys' moat was filled with leaves and brushwood instead of water. Any uninvited guest was sure to plunge through the loose branches into the ditch below.

"I just hope no one ever finds our hideout," Roswell continued.

"It's not likely," laughed Eugene. "No one knows our castle is here."

"Joey and Timmy know we are meeting somewhere here in the forest," James said unexpectedly. "I heard them talking about it one day when I was trying to sneak out here."

"Why do you fellows think I decided to build a moat?" Eugene asked.

"Because every castle has one," James replied. "We want this like a real castle."

"That's not the only reason," Eugene said.

"I wanted a moat because I was sure the younger boys would follow us here some day. Wouldn't it be funny to see Joey and Timmy crash into the moat when they tried to find out where we went? It would serve them right."

"They wouldn't get hurt, would they?" Roswell asked anxiously.

"No, of course not. The moat isn't that deep, and the branches wouldn't let them fall fast," Eugene assured him.

"That's good," James said. "I wouldn't want anyone to get hurt."

For two years the castle in the woods was the boys' favorite hiding place. Whenever they were scolded, they hurried to their retreat. Whenever the smaller boys bothered them, the older ones could soon lose their younger companions in the forest.

One hot day Eugene had not been able to recite a single lesson correctly. He had been scolded soundly, and he was cross. The other boys were restless, too.

As they left the schoolroom, Eugene motioned for the older boys to go outdoors. He hated walls and rooms. He liked to be sitting on the grass under a tree, looking up at the leaves, swaying in the breeze.

"Oh, bother!" he exclaimed. "There come those tadpoles, Joey and Timmy."

"Why do they always have to follow us?" demanded James. "Why don't they let us alone?"

"Let's run away from them," Eugene said.

"Sure, why not?" exclaimed the others. "Come on. Let's run to the castle!"

"Maybe they'll go all the way into the woods this time and fall into the moat," Eugene gloated. "It would serve them right."

"They won't, though. They never do," James said. "They always stop long before they get this far in the woods."

Off the older boys ran, intending to get away from the smaller ones. After them raced the little boys, who were getting bolder.

Mr. Tufts watched from a window. "There they go," he said to Mrs. Tufts. "The four big boys are running into the forest. The two smaller ones are trying to follow them again."

"It's good exercise for all of them," Mrs. Tufts said approvingly. "It's all right just so the younger boys don't go too far into the woods. They might get lost if they don't find the older boys."

"They never have yet," her husband said. He stood up in order to see better. The small boys seemed to be going farther than they ever had before. They might get lost.

"Joey, Timmy, come back!" he called sharply. "That's far enough!"

Since the boys couldn't hear him, they ran on. This time they were determined to catch up with the big boys. For a long time they had wanted to find out what it was that the older boys found so interesting in the woods. When the big boys ran, the smaller ones ran after them. It was no longer easy, as it had formerly been, to escape from the younger boys.

"Oh, dear, I suppose I should go after them," Mr. Tufts sighed. He, too, felt the heat. He wanted to rest. He did not want to hurry after two small boys.

"Yes, you really should, dear," his wife said firmly. "Timmy got a really bad case of poison ivy last year."

Mr. Tufts was sure the children would turn back before long. Farther and farther he pushed along the overgrown path. He thought he could hear them just ahead of him. With a final burst of speed, he dashed through the bushes.

There was a loud crash. A small cloud of dried leaves, green leaves, twigs, and branches rose from the moat. Four horrified older boys watched the waving arms and thrashing legs of Mr. Tufts as he sank down. They could hear his cough as the dust half choked him.

"Oh, no!" cried Roswell.

"Not Mr. Tufts!" wailed Ernest.

"How in the world did he get here?" asked James. "I though the little boys were coming. I never thought of Mr. Tufts!"

Eugene said nothing. His heart was beating wildly. He had never meant for Mr. Tufts to fall into the moat. What if the old man had been hurt? Old people's bones broke more easily than children's, Lizzie had often said. Once more Eugene's plans had turned out wrong.

Slowly he dragged his feet over to the moat. Slowly he began pulling branches away so that he could see into the trench. He almost hated to look. What if Mr. Tufts were dead?

But Mr. Tufts was far from dead. Sputtering

and coughing, he stood up. With Eugene's help, he climbed out of the moat. His face was very solemn and red as he spoke to the four boys.

"This is a most dangerous thing to have hidden in the woods," he said severely. "I might have been badly hurt. If Joey and Timmy had fallen into it, they couldn't have gotten out. A small boy would have been badly frightened. even if he was not injured."

The boys looked at the ground. They did not dare look at one another.

"I am deeply distressed that such a thing could happen," Mr. Tufts went on. He coughed again. "I might have been badly bruised! I might have suffered a broken bone!"

Eugene couldn't stand any more. "Oh, sir," he stammered. "R-really I did not mean for such a thing to happen. Believe me, s-sir, I didn't, really."

He seemed to be so upset that the schoolmaster

believed him. Yet this was more than a harmless prank. For the boy's own good, something had to be done.

"Eugene," he said firmly, "I have consulted your father already about your entrance into college. You are getting too old for this sort of thing. You like to play jokes, and you like to day-dream. You seem unable to settle down to serious study here."

Eugene sighed. This prank had been the straw that broke the camel's back. Now he would be sent away to a college where he'd have to study indoors all the time.

There were so many things he would rather do than go to college. He didn't want to be cooped up in a dusty old school. He wanted to travel and to see how other people ate, talked and lived. He didn't want just to read about these places and people.

"Some day I'm going to Europe," he said, his

voice dreamy. "Some day I'm going to visit France and Italy. You'll see."

Mr. Tufts hadn't expected this sort of reply. He did not understand the boy. Why, Eugene was smiling as if he had forgotten this incident and was already seeing foreign wonders.

"That's quite enough, Eugene," he said sharply. "You must learn to live in the present, not in your dreams. If you do not have what you like, you must like what you have."

He turned to the other boys. "Come, we must look for Joey and Timmy. They may be lost."

"No, they aren't, Mr. Tufts. Here they come now," James said happily. He had not wanted to search the forest on such a hot day. He was glad they had heard the noise Mr. Tufts made when he fell into the moat.

Eugene was still thinking about the time when he could leave school and travel.

"Maybe I'll even see Ireland!" he murmured.

Tired Feet and
an Empty Purse

"WHAT IS THAT noise?" asked Edgar Comstock.
He was a friend Eugene Field had made at
college in Columbia, Missouri.

"It sounds like a scared dog to me," Eugene
answered thoughtfully.

The two young men were traveling in Italy.
They had spent six fun-filled months in England,
Ireland, France, and Germany. Eugene's father
had died, and Eugene had spent almost all the
money he had inherited. Eugene was planning
to return home soon. However, he and Edgar
had no money for tickets. They had wired Mr.
Gray, Eugene's guardian, for more money, but

they had not yet received an answer. Now, as they walked in the bright Italian sunlight, they had heard something that bothered them.

"It sounded like a dog that is being beaten," Edgar said. He looked at Eugene's thin face. He knew his friend couldn't bear seeing an animal mistreated.

"Come on!" Eugene exclaimed. "Let's help that dog. It's being hurt!"

They ran back along the woodland path they'd been following. As they burst out of the woods, they saw a laughing crowd gathered near a crossroad. The yelping came from a tiny white puppy. He was trying to get away from a big, black-haired bully with a whip. The crowd cut off the small dog's escape. The bully snapped the whip close to the puppy's tail. The puppy jumped and yelled in fear. The crowd laughed, and the bully snapped his whip again.

"That's a terrible way to treat that poor little

pup!" Eugene exclaimed angrily. "See now the poor little creature is trembling!"

"They're not really hurting it," Edgar said. "They're not touching it with the whip."

"The little thing is terrified, hurt or not," Eugene snapped. "We'll have to stop those people from being so cruel."

"We can't do anything. There are too many of them and only two of us." Edgar was afraid of the huge, black-bearded man, who looked as if he might whip any stranger who tried to interfere with his sport.

Just then a carriage was stopped nearby. Edgar recognized the two women who were in it. They were guests at the hotel where he and Eugene were staying. The women seemed to be almost as upset as Eugene was.

"Come on, Eugene," Edgar pleaded. "We don't want to get into trouble over a dog."

Eugene shook Edgar's hand off his shoulder.

"Let it go!" he shouted, forgetting that no one would understand him.

The big man looked at Eugene in surprise. His whip dropped to his side. Eugene stooped and tucked the small dog under his arm.

Everyone in the crowd seemed to start yelling at once. The only word Eugene and Edgar understood was "Americano." This word was being said in a most unfriendly way. The crowd kept pressing closer to the young Americans and surrounded them.

"Let's get out of here," Eugene said.

"That's a good idea," Edgar said. "How?"

Eugene looked over the angry faces. "I don't understand Italian, but expressions are the same in any language," he said.

"Put the dog down. Maybe they think we are trying to steal it."

Eugene set the puppy down, but the crowd still looked threatening.

172

"I guess they're angry with us about something else," Edgar said. "The only Italian words we know are 'buon giorno' and 'grazie,' but it isn't a good morning and there's certainly nothing to thank them for!"

"Probably they're angry because we broke up their sport," Eugene said. "It's like going to Spain and breaking up a bullfight."

"You'd never get out with a bull under your arm," Edgar said.

The puppy had tucked its tail between its legs and quietly disappeared. Now the man with the whip came toward Eugene, clearing a path through the crowd with his swinging whip. His face was twisted in angry lines.

Eugene and Edgar looked around desperately. The carriage they had seen earlier was moving in their direction. Someone opened the door and they heard a crisp English voice saying, "Get in quickly."

174

Eugene and Edgar did not hesitate. As they jumped into the carriage the woman who had spoken to them addressed a stream of rapid Italian toward the crowd. The Americans had no idea what she said, but the excited men immediately stood back from the carriage.

The young men relaxed against the cushions as the horse trotted down the road. For the first time they looked at the two well-dressed women who had rescued them. The one who had scattered the crowd seemed to be enjoying the adventure. The other was trembling.

"Thank you for saving our lives!" Eugene said earnestly. He hadn't thought that trying to help a dog could cause so much trouble.

Edgar was hoping that Mr. Gray would not send them any more money. It was not that he hadn't had fun being Eugene's guest. It was just that they always managed to get into some sort of trouble in every country.

When they reached their Italian hotel, the clerk handed them two letters. Mr. Gray had written to inform them that he could not supply them any more money.

"We'll just have to sell all the souvenirs we've bought," Edgar suggested.

"Oh, no!" Eugene protested. "I just couldn't sell all my wonderful souvenirs!" He had started another collection.

But Edgar was right. To buy even third-class tickets they had to sell almost all the souvenirs they had purchased during the trip.

The second letter was from Julia, Edgar's younger sister. When Eugene was in college, he had often visited in the Comstock home in St. Joseph, Missouri. Of all Edgar's sisters, Julia was Eugene's favorite.

"Did Julia mention me?" Eugene asked.

"She asks if you've made up your mind about what you'll do when you return home."

"Oh," said Eugene unenthusiastically. The sparkle left his eyes.

"Well?" asked Edgar. "Haven't you?"

"I've seen Europe just as I said I would," Eugene answered shortly.

"Yes, that's true, and you've spent all the money your father left you. Now how do you plan to earn a living? What kind of job will you look for?" Edgar knew that Julia and Eugene liked each other very much and that they planned to marry some day.

"I guess I should have finished college," admitted Eugene, looking serious. "It would have made job hunting easier. But I just don't know what I want to do."

"It's more important to know what you can do," Edgar told him.

"Oh, I know what I can do. I can draw a little, write a little, act a little, and speak a little. But how can I get a job?"

"You really do have a gift for writing," Edgar said thoughtfully. "Remember all the plays you wrote in college?"

"Yes, but what I wanted to do was to act in them," Eugene said, laughing. "Do you remember how terrible my acting was?"

"That's true," Edgar agreed, "but everyone liked your writing. While you were a sophomore you sent articles in to the newspapers, didn't you?"

"Yes, I did," said Eugene. "I did like writing them, too."

"Then why not look for a reporter's job?"

"Why not, indeed," Eugene agreed. "Come on, Edgar, let's pack and go home."

He counted his scanty supply of money. "I have just enough left to buy Julia a little French poodle," he said happily.

He thought for a moment. "I shall call the dog McSweeney."

The Famous
Mr. Field

John Barry's ten-year-old legs could hardly keep up with his father's long strides.

"You're very lucky to be able to meet Eugene Field, John," his father said. "He's a very famous man. I've only met him once, but when I told him you liked his poems and were writing a theme about him in school, he told me to bring you to his home. He said he'd like to see you and talk with you."

"Does he have a long beard like Henry Wadsworth Longfellow?" asked John eagerly. "Is he a very old man?"

"The answer to both questions is no," said Mr.

Barry. "But you'll soon see for yourself. That's the Field house across the street."

They stopped and looked at the big house with its many windows and chimneys. Then they crossed the street and turned up the walk leading to the front door.

"I'm sure I don't need to tell you to be on your best behavior," said Mr. Barry.

"I'll only speak when I'm spoken to," promised John. He wondered if he'd know what to say to such a famous man when he was spoken to.

Would a servant open the door or would Eugene Field himself do it? John tried to stay a few steps in back of his father.

The bell echoed through the house. Could they have come on the wrong day? Suddenly the door was thrown open by a small blond boy. He was breathless, and his shirt hung out of his trousers. "Come in," he said. "Father's up in the cupola braying for Don Caesar. He's the

180

only one who can. Excuse me." The boy hurried down the hall.

"Did he say braying?" asked John.

"I thought so," said his father, "but we must have misunderstood him."

In a moment the blond boy raced back through the hall and up the stairs, shouting, "It's all right, Father. Trotty's got him."

"Did you ever see so many clocks?" asked John, looking around the big hallway. There were clocks on the wall and on tables and on the stairway. All of them were ticking, but none of them agreed. One said two o'clock, one said ten minutes after two, two said two-thirty, and one said nine-forty.

Mr. Barry and John were not alone very long. In a moment a small girl came wandering into the hall with an armload of books.

"Who are you?' " she asked. "I'm Posy Field. Would you like to hear me say, 'Twas the night

181

before Christmas and all through the house——"

"I see Posy is entertaining you," said a deep voice behind them. "I'm very glad you came."

John thought he had never before seen such intense blue eyes as this man had. The man also had lines around his eyes and his mouth which showed that he often smiled.

"I'm sorry to have kept you waiting," said Mr. Field, "but we have a very evil donkey that won't stay in his own yard. The neighbors complain about his appetite for flowers and rose bushes when he gets loose, so we try to get him home as soon as we can. If I go up to the cupola on top of the house and bray, he usually answers. Then the boys can tell where he is and get him. I'm really quite good at braying," he remarked, smiling modestly.

"Not a creature was stirring, not even a mouse," Posey said impatiently.

"I can't imagine why we keep Don Caesar any-

way," said Mr. Field. "In one of his better weeks he ate a hundred pounds of hay, a peck of corn on the cob, a bushel of oats, three pies, a layer cake, and Jessie Chapman's parasol. Do come into my study."

After Mr. Field closed his study door they could still hear Posy reciting, "And laying his finger beside of his nose————"

John had never seen such a room. There were books everywhere, on shelves from the floor to the ceiling and piled in stacks on the floor. There was a shelf crowded with empty bottles of every size and shape. There were shelves of shells and shelves of mechanical toy animals. Here and again there were clocks, old and new, each one ticking and keeping its own time.

"I like to collect things," said Mr. Field, "especially books and clocks. When I was a boy people were always trying to tell me it was better to collect just one thing. I didn't believe it then, and I don't believe it now. I'm interested in a great many things."

"What all do you collect, Mr. Field?" asked John. He had forgotten about speaking only when he was spoken to.

"Canes, warming pans, moths—anything that interests me," answered Mr. Field. "Perhaps you'd like to see them before you leave."

"Oh, I would," said John.

"Are there any questions you want to ask?"

"What made you want to write?" asked John.

"My grandmother paid me for my first writing when I was about your age," Mr. Field said. "It was a sermon. I probably worked as hard on that as on anything I have written since."

"Have you always written for newspapers since you were grown up?" John asked.

"Sometimes I'm not sure I'm entirely grown up. My first job was writing for the Denver Tribune, but I wasn't cut out to be a reporter.

The editor complained that I used my imagination to save my legs. People never could tell exactly where my facts left off and my imagination began."

"Mr. Field doesn't seem at all like a famous man," John said after they had left the house. "He's so nice and funny."

"Eugene Field probably does more funny things than most people, famous or not," Mr. Barry said. "One time before he was successful he felt that he should have a larger salary. When his editor refused him, he dressed four of his children in rags and brought them to the office. They all fell on their knees and pretended to cry while Mr. Field said, 'Please, Mr. Stone, can't you see your way clear to raising my salary?'"

"It must be fun to live with a man like Mr. Field," said John. "You'd never be sure what would happen next."

"I'm sure you wouldn't," said Mr. Barry.

Eugene Field Day

"What poem did you choose, Mary?" Miss Black asked. The year was 1897, and the pupils were honoring their favorite poet, Eugene Field.

"I chose 'Little Boy Blue,'" said Mary.

"The little toy dog is covered with dust,
But sturdy and staunch he stands;
And the little toy soldier is red with rust,
And his musket moulds in his hands.
Time was when the little toy dog was new
And the soldier was passing fair,
And that was the time when our Little Boy
     Blue
Kissed them and put them there.
'Now don't you go till I come,' he said,
'And don't you make any noise!'
So toddling off to his trundle-bed
He dreamt of the pretty toys."

After Mary had read the complete poem, Miss Black said, "Mr. Field might have been feeling sad, thinking of his own son who died young, when he wrote that poem."

"I like Mr. Field's funny poems better than his sad ones," said a red-haired boy. "May I read 'Jest 'Fore Christmas'?"

"Yes, I think we all like that one."

The boy stood up and began to read.

"Father calls me William, sister calls me Will.
Mother calls me Willie, but the fellers call me Bill!
Mighty glad I ain't a girl—ruther be a boy,
Without them sashes, curls an' things that's worn by Fauntleroy!
Love to chawnk green apples an' go swimmin' in the lake——
Hate to take the caster-ile they give for belly-ache!
'Most all the time, the whole year round, there ain't no flies on me,
But jest 'fore Christmas I'm as good as I kin be!"

188

"I know another funny one," said a tall, thin boy. "It's called 'Seein' Things.'"

"We'd like to hear it, Arthur."

Arthur began to read the poem.

"I aint afeared uv snakes, or toads, or bugs, or
    worms or mice,
An' things 'at girls are skeered uv I think are
    awful nice!
I'm pretty brave, I guess; an' yet I hate to go
    to bed,
For, when I'm tucked up warm an' snug an'
    when my prayers are said,
Mother tells me 'Happy dreams!' and takes
    away the light,
An' leaves me lyin' all alone an' seein' things
    at night!"

"I think Eugene Field must have known what it was like to be afraid at night when he was a boy," Miss Black said. "Perhaps that's why he wrote so many lullabies during his lifetime. Didn't anyone bring a lullaby?"

189

When Polly raised her hand, Miss Black asked, "Would you read your lullaby, Polly?"

"Oh, I don't need to read it," said Polly. "Mother used to sing it to me nearly every night, and I know it by heart." She recited,

"Wynken, Blynken, and Nod one night
Sailed off in a wooden shoe—
Sailed on a river of crystal light,
Into a sea of dew.
'Where are you going, and what do you wish?'
The old moon asked the three.
'We have come to fish for the herring fish
That live in this beautiful sea;
Nets of silver and gold have we!'
Said Wynken, Blynken and Nod."

"My favorite is 'The Duel,'" said a little girl in a starched white pinafore. "I found it in a special book of poems."

"Will you please read the poem to us from the book?" Miss Black requested.

The little girl rose from her seat and read in a clear, sweet voice.

"The gingham dog and the calico cat
  Side by side on the table sat;
  'Twas half-past twelve, and (what do you
      think!)
  Nor one nor t'other had slept a wink!
  The old Dutch clock and the Chinese plate
  Appeared to know as sure as fate
  There was going to be a terrible spat.
  (I wasn't there; I simply state
  What was told to me by the Chinese plate!)

  The gingham dog went 'Bow-wow-wow!'
  And the calico cat replied 'Mee-ow!'
  The air was littered an hour or so,
  With bits of gingham and calico,
  While the old Dutch clock in the chimney place
  Up with its hands before its face,
  For it always dreaded a family row!
  (Now mind, I'm only telling you
  What the old Dutch clock declares is true!)"

"We have enjoyed hearing these poems by Eugene Field, and I'm sure you will want to read more of his verses from the books in the library," said Miss Black. "Now I want to show you a picture which illustrates the gingham dog and the calico cat."

This is the picture she showed the class.

More About This Book

WHEN EUGENE FIELD LIVED

1850   EUGENE FIELD WAS BORN IN ST. LOUIS, MISSOURI, SEPTEMBER 2 OR 3.

There were thirty states in the Union.

Millard Fillmore was President.

The population of the country was approximately 23,190,000.

1850–   EUGENE GREW UP IN ST. LOUIS, MISSOURI, AND
1865   AMHERST, MASSACHUSETTS.

California became a state, 1852.

The Lincoln-Douglas debates were held, 1858.

Eleven States seceded from the Union and formed the Confederate States of America, 1860-1861.

The War between the States was fought, 1861-1865.

President Lincoln issued the Emancipation Proclamation, 1863.

The first Pullman sleeping car was built, 1864.

1865– 1873	EUGENE ATTENDED COLLEGE AND AFTERWARD MADE A TRIP TO EUROPE.

President Lincoln was assassinated, and Andrew Johnson became President, 1865.

The United States purchased Alaska, 1867.

The first transcontinental railroad was completed, 1869.

A great fire destroyed most of Chicago, 1871.

1873– 1883	FIELD SERVED AS A COLUMNIST ON SEVERAL MID-WESTERN NEWSPAPERS.

Alexander Graham Bell invented the telephone, 1876.

Thomas Edison invented the phonograph, 1878, and the electric light bulb, 1879.

James A. Garfield became President and was assassinated, 1881.

1883– 1895	FIELD BECAME A NEWSPAPER COLUMNIST IN CHICAGO AND WROTE MANY BOOKS.

The first elevated street railway in the United States was operated in Baltimore, 1885.

The Statue of Liberty was unveiled in New York, 1886.

Henry Ford built his first gas engine, 1893.

194

1895   EUGENE FIELD DIED IN BUENA PARK, ILLINOIS,
      NOVEMBER 4.

There were forty-two states in the Union.

Grover Cleveland was President.

The population of the country was approximately 62,950,000.

DO YOU REMEMBER?

1. How did the housekeeper Temperance entertain Eugene and Roswell?

2. How did Eugene get into trouble frequently after he and Roswell moved to Amherst?

3. What happened to Harry Brown when Eugene and Roswell played with him in the church?

4. How did Eugene's pet mouse cause trouble at Grandmother Field's home?

5. How did Grandmother Field help the boys to earn money for fishing poles?

6. Why was Eugene excited about his Grandfather's museum in the back yard?

7. Why did Eugene decide to tear up the newspaper which he and Roswell prepared?

8. What happened when the children of Amherst presented a play in the Boltwood barn?

9. How did Eugene and Roswell attempt to send cakes to a soldier in the Union Army?

10. Why was Eugene homesick after he and Roswell went to Mr. Tufts' school?

11. How were Eugene and his friend Edgar rescued from an angry crowd in Italy?

12. How did Eugene and Edgar manage to return to the United States from Europe?

13. How did Mr. Field explain why he made writing his life work?

14. What are the names of some of Eugene Field's most popular poems?

IT'S FUN TO LOOK UP THESE THINGS

1. Who is a newspaper columnist, and how does he differ from a reporter?

2. What persons write columns for the newspaper that you frequently read?

3. How does poetry such as Field wrote differ from prose, as in a story book?

196

4. How can you tell whether a story or poem is true or whether it is make-believe?

5. Why would you say that Eugene Field frequently is called the Poet of Childhood?

6. What other poets besides Field have written poems especially for children?

INTERESTING THINGS YOU CAN DO

1. Make a list of Field's poems which you have read or would like to read.

2. Collect illustrations from Field's poems for a display on the bulletin board.

3. Choose one of Field's poems to read aloud to the class.

4. Read one of Field's poems and rewrite it in the form of a story.

5. Compare Field's poems with the poems written by another popular author.

6. Write a four-line poem about an animal to share with your classmates.

7. Start a scrapbook made up of your favorite poems, including some by Field.

OTHER BOOKS YOU MAY ENJOY READING

American Butterflies and Moths, Cecile Matschat. Random House.

Favorite Fairy Tales Told in Ireland, Virginia Haviland. Little-Brown.

Hailstones and Halibut Bones, Mary O'Neil. Doubleday.

Kate Douglas Wiggin: The Little Schoolteacher, Miriam E. Mason. Trade and School Editions, Bobbs-Merrill.

My Hobby Is Collecting Rocks and Minerals, David Jensen. Grosset.

Squire for King Arthur, Eugenia Stone. Follett.

Time for Poetry, May Hill Arbuthnot, ed. Scott, Foresman.

INTERESTING WORDS IN THIS BOOK

banshee (băn′shē) : Irish fairy believed to warn a family of an approaching death

belfry (bĕl′frĭ) : tower in a church or other building which houses large bell

benevolent (bė̇ nĕv′ȯ lĕnt) : kindhearted

bray (brā) : make a harsh cry, as a mule or donkey

brocade (brȯ kād′) : heavy cloth with woven raised decorative design

cello (chĕl′lō) : musical instrument like a violin, but much larger

critical (krĭt′ĭ kăl) : faultfinding

cupola (kū′pȯ là) : dome or rounded room atop a building

damsel (dăm′zĕl) : girl

foolhardy (fōōl′här′dĭ) : daring, reckless, bold

gallant (găl′ănt) : noble, brave

gremlin (grĕm′lĭn) : impish foot-high little fellow who brings trouble

hubbub (hŭb′ŭb) : uproar, din

incident (ĭn′sĭ dĕnt) : event, happening

leprechaun (lĕp′rĕ̆ kôn) : Irish fairy, supposed to know of a hidden pot of gold

livery stable (lĭv′ĕr ĭ stā′b′l) : barn where horses and carriages are kept to be rented

nimbly (nĭm′blĭ) : in a lively manner, swiftly

outlandish (out lăn′dĭsh) : strange, unusual

pixie (pĭk′sĭ) : fairy

rheumatism (rōō′mà tĭz′m) : painful disease of joints

rousing (rouz′ing) : exciting

sanctuary (săngk′tủ â′rĭ) : safe place

scepter (sĕp′tẽr) : staff carried by a ruler as a symbol of authority

scrape (skrāp) : predicament which a person brings on himself in some manner

scroll (skrōl) : roll of paper

shilling (shĭl′lĭng) : British silver coin

shudder (shŭd′ẽr) : tremble, shiver

souvenir (sōō′vĕ nẽr′) : memento, keepsake

stately (stāt′lĭ) : dignified, grand

superstition (sū′pẽr stĭsh′ŭn) : belief or practice founded on ignorance and fear

taffy pull (tăf′ĭ) : party where candy is made

text (tĕkst) : verse or topic which a minister uses as a subject for his sermon

tiara (tī âr′á) : crownlike head ornament

turban (tûr′băn) : hat or cap with a cloth wound around it

underground railway: secret means of escape for slaves during War between the States

viola (vẻ ō′là) : musical instrument with strings, resembling a violin

2909